POISONING MISADVENTURES

Narrative Excerpts on Food-Borne Diseases and Poisoning for the Physician, Microbiologist, Attorney and Nutritionist

POISONING MISADVENTURES

Narrative Excerpts on Food-Borne Diseases and Poisoning for
the Physician, Microbiologist, Attorney and Nutritionist

By

LLOYD BRYAN JENSEN

*Formerly: Instructor, The University of Chicago; First Assistant and
Assistant Professor, Department of Experimental Microbiology, Mayo Clinic
and Foundation; Consultant, Walter Reed Army Institute of Research,
Washington, D. C.; Lecturer, U.S. Public Health Service, C.D.C. Training
Branch, Atlanta; Member, Liaison and Scientific Advisory Board of the
Quartermaster Food and Container Institute for the Armed Forces*

CHARLES C THOMAS · PUBLISHER

Springfield · Illinois · U.S.A.

Published and Distributed Throughout the World by
CHARLES C THOMAS • PUBLISHER
BANNERSTONE HOUSE
301-327 East Lawrence Avenue, Springfield, Illinois, U.S.A.
NATCHEZ PLANTATION HOUSE
735 North Atlantic Boulevard, Fort Lauderdale, Florida, U.S.A.

© *1970, by* CHARLES C THOMAS • PUBLISHER
Library of Congress Catalog Card Number: 78-128647

With THOMAS BOOKS *careful attention is given to all details of
manufacturing and design. It is the Publisher's desire to present books
that are satisfactory as to their physical qualities and artistic possibilities
and appropriate for their particular use.* THOMAS BOOKS *will be true
to those laws of quality that assure a good name and good will.*

Printed in the United States of America
I-1

To My Wife
FRANCES McMAHON JENSEN
This Book Is
Affectionately Dedicated

PREFACE

W HILE SORTING AND discarding a voluminous accumulation of notes and personal laboratory data on food-borne illness and poisoning, which we have acquired over fifty years of service, the thought occurred that brief narrative excerpts of this material might be of passing interest to students, laymen, and a host of people engaged or versed in these fields, both civilian and Armed Services personnel. Perhaps some of the sections in both Parts I and II can provide sidelights in the total field as reference material or historical footnotes.

The involved scientific aspects of these areas need not be presented here in competition with the excellent textbooks, monographs, and journal literature now extant. Therefore, none of the subjects in our purview is treated exhaustively or conventionally nor does it need to be. Our hope and intent is to partially illuminate an old horizon in this manner, that is to say, by anecdote, personal observations in camp and on battlefield, in litigation, by stirring up and laying of archival dust and so on, in many more categories.

Should some of our statements sound subjective in tone and meaning, we shall plead *nolo contendere*, as veterans who have done their best are prone to do if and when confronted with flagellating words and phrases.

To any vision must be brought an eye adapted to what is to be seen.

—Plotinus to his pupil, Porphyry of Tyre.

CONTENTS

Page

Preface vii

Part I. Bacterial Poisons

INTRODUCTION 5

THE CIVIL WAR: FOOD-BORNE INFECTIONS 8

THE ROCKY MOUNTAIN MEN 16

THE PASSENGER PIGEONS AND DISEASE 23

SOME BIZARRE VIEWS OF FOODS IN THE PAST 26

STAPHYLOCOCCI 34

SALMONELLAE 56

THE ROLE OF STREPTOCOCCI (LANCEFIELD TYPE D) IN
    FOOD-BORNE GASTROENTERITIS 60

BOTULISM 64

GENUS BACILLUS 72

CLOSTRIDIUM PERFRINGENS 72

FOOD-BORNE VIRAL DISEASES, INCLUDING HEPATITIS 74

VOMITING AND DIARRHEA NOT CAUSED BY FOOD-POISONING
    BACTERIA 77

UNCERTAIN ETIOLOGIES 81

LUMINOUS FOODS AND PHOSPHORESCENT BACTERIA 83

TRICHINOSIS AND FOOD TABOOS OF SEMITIC AND NEAR
    EASTERN NATIONS 84

INHERENT TOXICITY OF NATURAL PRODUCTS MISTAKENLY
    USED AS FOODS 96

Part II. Vegetal and Mineral Poisons

INTRODUCTION 103

POISONS IN THE GRECO-ROMAN WORLD 105

ANTIDOTES FOR POISONS IN ANCIENT TIMES 112

WINE, MEAD AND BEER IN ANCIENT TIMES 117

HEMLOCK: THE SOCRATIC POISON 121

NUX VOMICA AND CLEOPATRA'S EXPERIMENTS 124

BELLADONNA LEAVES 126

HENBANE (HYOSCYAMUS) 127

POISONOUS MUSHROOMS 128

CASTOR BEAN POISONS 131

OPIUM AND THE CAVE OF BATS 133

ACONITE 135

COLCHICINE (COLCHIUM) AND THE SYRIAN HAMSTER 137

THE ASSASSINS AND CANNABIS INDICA—SATIVA 139

NICOTINE, THE FIRST CIGARETTE, AND SHAH ABBAS 143

CARBON MONOXIDE (CO) 146

BROKEN GLASS AND POWDERED DIAMOND IN FOOD AND DRINK 151

ARSENIC AND THE MURDER OF NAPOLEON 158

LEAD POISONING AND BIRD-SHOT IN GAME 165

MERCURY 169

ANTIMONY 171

CADMIUM 173

BARIUM 174

THE CYANIDES 175

SODIUM FLUORIDE 178

SULFITES AND 4,000 YEAR-OLD PRESERVED MEAT AT JERICHO 180

A FLEETING NOTE ON ANCIENT TEMPLE MEATS FROM
    SACRIFICES 185

Index 193

POISONING MISADVENTURES

Narrative Excerpts on Food-Borne Diseases and Poisoning for
the Physician, Microbiologist, Attorney and Nutritionist

I
Bacterial
Poisons

INTRODUCTION

MAN OF THE SEVERAL species in search of food over a vast expanse of time during the Pleistocene and Holocene epochs, experienced a great deal of poisoning. Obviously, no one knows how many individuals of the genus *Homo* were poisoned by mushrooms, nightshade, or deceptive berries. Primal man learned that certain fruits, nuts, berries, leaves, roots, grains, fungi, shellfish, snails, eels, and other fish could, upon ingestion, cause diarrhea, vomiting, convulsions, and even death. Also, outcrops of some surface minerals, stings of arthropods, and bites of venomous snakes could cause illness and death.

Archaeologists and anthropologists find from their evidence in unearthed assemblages of the far-distant past as well as from study of living primal man that early (and present) food gatherers were toxicologists of no mean ability. This was true, especially in preparation of arrow poisons, and, strangely enough, in case of their empirical complex methods for detoxifications of cyanide-containing manioc and other deadly vegetal tissues.[1] We shall elaborate on this later, when we discuss poisons from the mineral, vegetable, and animal sources known to the protoliterate and literate ancients sometime after the third millenium. It might be sufficient to state that poisoners of the recorded past of the Near Eastern, Greek, Hellenistic, and Roman worlds had developed their criminal art to a high degree of lethal efficacy. The active principles of the toxic agents were obviously unknown for the most part, excepting, of course, sources of certain poisons used with criminal intent. Quite important to the ancients were the deviltries attributed to their gods and demons, including voodoo and witchcraft practices.

With the rise of modern science, much was learned of

---

[1]Jensen, L. B.: *Man's Foods: Nutrition and Environments in Food Gathering Times and Food Producing Times.* Champaign, Garrard Press, 1953, pp. 166-168.

causal agents in food poisonings and infections, and the tempo of discoveries has accelerated at a truly remarkable pace these past few decades. Today, few causes of outbreaks of gastro-intestinal "irritations" (to use the mild term) go unresolved, theoretically at least. Episodes of sporadic cases, called incidents, may on occasion escape notice and thus remain obscure so far as factual data are desired by the epidemiologist and statistician.

The extent of food-borne disease occurring in outbreaks and episodes has not abated in this country, however great our knowledge may be, encompassing as it now does many of the factors of cause and prevention. For instance, the National Office of Vital Statistics of the Public Health Service reported that during 1959, there were 24 million cases of acute gastro-intestinal disease, resulting in 336 million days lost as bed cases—an incidence of 14,000 per 100,000 population! This statistically dismal situation is not attributable to the never-ceasing vigilance of public health officials but rather to educability of people involved in the complex food-beverage picture "right up to the mouth of the consumer." From this point on, i.e. ingestion, a peccant food enters the alimentary canal, and the aftermath falls into categories of the "Anatomy of Melancholy." The literature on these subjects is now deservedly voluminous, with excellent textbooks, monographs, bulletins, and journal articles available to all through many conventional and accepted sources. It would be gratuitous, if not impossible, to list here the immense numbers of these titles.

The object of the present writer, now in retirement after nearly a half-century of buffeting in these turbulent fields, is to record readings from the literature of antiquity and the more recent past, some laboratory researches and examinations, instances of army and civilian field work as an epidemiologist, and odd courtroom incidents selected from over four hundred trials of cases (and as many depositions) in which we served as a science witness. We have experienced both sad and humorous situations which arose in our work. Undoubtedly, everyone in this type of work has had parallel experiences, differing only in variety, since the field is governed by "Murphy's" overriding law: "If anything can go wrong, it will."

A story circulating during the antebellum days (before the War Between the States) told to us in 1914 by a veteran of the 7th Mississippi Battery of 1864, pointed up our problem obliquely. "An old pious aunt of the youthful bride-to-be cautioned (as a duenna should) the innocent prospective bride with the then-deliciate admonition, 'There is a side to men's nature, my dear, that is women's burden to bear.'" So it is with certain foods and beverages serving as vectors that may be our burden to bear. Long ago, when we were beginners in this field, the late Professor Edwin Oakes Jordan of the University of Chicago told us, "What is wanted in food and drink is innocence rather than repentance."

THE CIVIL WAR: FOOD-BORNE
INFECTIONS

MANY OF US BORN in the latter part of the nineteenth century were privileged to talk to the aging Civil War veterans, both of the North and South. These intrepid old soldiers were always glad to accommodate inquiring youth with information about their personal experiences during those stirring but bloody years of 1861 to 1865. Never was a word of rancor heard against either side so far as combat soldiers were concerned, but sutlers, commissary agents, substitute-buying men, and the mine run of political generals came in for remarks which seemed preserved in strong vinegar and brimstone.

Gastrointestinal diseases were rife in both armies, we learned and, to an extent, not generally appreciated by the conventional historian. Obviously, the microbiologic nature of food- and water-borne illnesses was not well understood—if known at all—but chemical poisonings from sutlers' high-priced "delicacies" aroused the suspicion and ire of the knowing officer and private. Bacteriologic information of the period provided little technical assistance to the medical profession, since even Harvard Medical School had no microscope until 1869.

Outbreaks involving most members of a company, and even a regiment, were given highly descriptive names such as "Tennessee quickstep," "green-apple quickstep," "General Pope's headquarters' disease," "gallus busters," "green-corn rumbles," "death in the pot (II Kings 4:40)," "Bragg's drislies," and many more appellations of dubious clinical worth or preciseness. Most of these outbreaks were undoubtedly microbiologic in nature. To the present writer, this need not now be conjectural, because the veterans, both Blue and Gray, and a physician of the 36th Illinois Volunteers (2nd Division, 4th Corps), who was our family doctor said that many of those stricken from eating sutlers' wares became sick in a few minutes to a half hour (chemical poisoning), whereas symptoms of gastrointestinal and intestinal diseases in outbreaks set in at longer periods after eating the unprotected army food. Judging from the sketchy but salient data given us, the causal microbial agents were the same as we know them to be at the present time, namely, *Staphylococcus enterotoxin, Salmonella,* Lancefield group D *Streptococcus, Shigella,* and less certain, *Clostridium perfringens, Bacillus cereus,* and some of the viruses. Underprocessed canned foods were supplied to the Union armies, and botulism may have occurred, but we have no information from the conversations and records. When we discuss these entities later on, a plausible overall case for these assumptions can be made.

We are better off today in institutional and armed forces feeding, although outbreaks do occur. The modern soldier is not as brash, vocally at least, as his great, great-grandfather when a soldier boy of the Civil War, judging by the old story about the commanding Union officer who observed and heard his men "eating their food seasoned with honest growls." Lining up his men and drawing himself up to ramrod posture, this officer called out, "And what's wrong with army food?" A prompt answer resounded loud and clear from a private in the rear rank, "They won't tell us, Sir!"

The enterics (*Salmonellae, Shigella,* probably type D streptococci, and others to be discussed) became increasingly virulent as the war went on. *Salmonella typhi* in 1861 killed 17 per cent of patients, and by 1865 the mortality rate from typhoid fever was 56 per cent. The diarrhea and dysentery morbidity rate was 640 per 1,000 during the first year of the war, and rose to 995 per 1,000 in 1862![2] Bruce Catton once pointed out that simply being in the armies of the Civil War killed many more men than were killed in battle!

Military results at the first Battle of Bull Run were disheartening to the North but dismally sad to General McDowell

---

[2]Adams, G. W.: *Doctors in Blue: The Medical History of the Union Army in the Civil War.* New York, Collier Books, 1961 Chap. 10.

who then commanded the Union troops. The general suffered
food poisoning, apparently salmonellosis. He would dismount
quickly from his faithful charger, "yield to Nature's rumble,"
and hurriedly mount up, then dismount with greater alacrity.
Finally, his backquarters became so raw that he could not ride
his horse but had to race about the field in a wagon. The soldiers, as have been their wont for ages, made up a ballad: "His
headquarters was so sore," etc. This was no laughing matter,
and many an ill-fated boy was lost because of General McDowell's
suffering.

These soldiers of the Army of the Potomac fared little better
under General John Pope. Improvising lyrics for the tune
"When Johnny comes Marching Home," they sang:

> They gave us John Pope, our patience to tax,
>   Hurrah! Hurrah!
> His headquarters were in the saddle,
>   Hurrah! Hurrah!
> We are the boys of Patman's ranks
> We ran with McDowell, retreated with Banks,
> And we'll all drink stone blind,
> Johnny, fill up the bowl . . .

General Pope, when issuing reports to the troops, always dated
his directives with "Headquarters in the Saddle," which naturally sparked much wry humor in ballad form. One line only
will suffice to illustrate the refrain: "Pope's headquarters are
where his head should be. . . Oh! What a sick headache has
he," etc. One of the grim jokes of these soldiers, which carried
over to civilian life, was "bowels are of more importance than
brains in the Army."

It is now known that General Robert E. Lee at Gettysburg
suffered from either shigellosis or salmonellosis and was unable
to direct his army with his usual sagacity. On the third day of
the historic conflict, General Lee did no more than nod un-
decipherably to General Longstreet in a desperate decision for
Pickett's heroic but ill-fated charge. Longstreet himself was opposed to this action. Fully 10 per cent of the Confederate States
Army (CSA) rank and file were suffering and weakened from

dysentery during the three-day holocaust. Notwithstanding, the Army of Northern Virginia CSA was at its zenith in valor and devotion, and without dimming the glory of General Lee, one only recalls Sir Philip Sidney's remark, "An army of stags led by a lion is more formidable than an army of lions led by a stag." The great-hearted Lee did assume all responsibilities, and his words, "It is all my fault," made no allowance for his illness. These dysentery-causing bacilli impaired General Lee's judgement and vigor, according to the evidence now available to medical historians.

Most troops suffered severely, both the CSA in Pennsylvania and the Union Armies in the South. Some ascribed their "quicksteps" and fever to gorging, "bad water" and worse "likker," or an unaccustomed dietary regimen. Private Leander Stillwell of an Illinois regiment at Shiloh and nearby Pittsburg Landing attributed the widespread dysentery during that fateful six-week campaign to "eating too much sugar and improper rations." At Shiloh just before the battle, the Federals, suffering severe dysentery, grinned wanly and called it the Tennessee quickstep, whereas Private Chauncey Cook, 25th Wisconsin Volunteers, called it "the Kentucky quickstep." Officers of the 4th Minnesota Infantry, when their men complained about their undignified suffering in this way, yelled, "Try red-hot pokers; that's a sure cure!"

The idea of safe, potable water was unknown then and a long time aborning. Soldiers drank "clear" water from any source available: shallow wells, ponds, rivers, and runs. Dysenteries (salmonellosis, shigellosis, paracolon, and amoebic dysenteries) claimed more victories than did battles.

When Generals Grant and Sherman devised effective methods for "living off the country," their army rations were improved in quality and quantity. Before that time, when either salt beef or fresh beef was issued to the troops, when cooked it generally stank to high heaven, for it was often very "aged." Now and then, when an especially bad hunk of meat was served out, the men would organize a mock funeral, parading through camp with the offending beef on a bier and bury it with solemn ceremonies, "where the Colonel could see." (We know that salt does not inhibit toxicogenic staphylococci enough to prevent toxin formation.)

However, a Massachusetts soldier, T. W. Higginson, told of a West Point lieutenant who, when on routine inspection for weak spots in camp, smelled every camp kettle and food issue and evidently became unpopular with the cooks and K.P.'s. This, naturally, was a rare and isolated incident.

Data from many diaries and conversations with soldiers of the Civil War stressed causes of gastrointestinal distresses as due to badly handled and poorly prepared foods; beans half-cooked or baked were the chief offenders, according to Private Abner Small of the 16th Maine Volunteers.

"But many's the time we would have to 'get up and git' eating our beans half-cooked, and then would come an internal disturbance—not that infernal demon, dyspepsia, of civil life—but an almighty bellyache that would double a man up and down and send him into line at Surgeon's Call." This may have been *Staphylococcus* food poisoning from some other food. (Ancient Roman writers said that beans were fit food only for gladiators and blacksmiths.)

Bruce Catton quotes a Civil War soldier in the 4th Rhode Island Infantry who was bitter about the food given the sick and wounded; the mainstay, he said, was shadow soup. This soldier bequeathed the recipe to posterity: "Put a large kettle of water on to boil, then hang a chicken so that its shadow falls in the water, and boil the shadow for half an hour; add salt and pepper and serve." At least, this soup never caused bowel complaints. It had no staying qualities, but if partaken of too long might cause "soup edema" seen in areas of starvation during World War I.

Perhaps one of the most poignant stories of the Civil War was told long afterwards by GAR "boys" and recorded by Captain E. A. Wilson of Cleveland in 1893. On that awful field of death at Shiloh, the numerous dead, both North and South, could not be buried properly for a time, but merely laid in shallow trenches or lightly covered with earth. A few weeks after that holocaust, a young soldier in a western Union regiment, marching over the battlefield, broke ranks, ran out involuntarily, and placed a piece of hardtack biscuit in an empty hand groping for the sky. The boys in blue and gray were always hungry; hence, their preoccupation with food in their letters home and their bitter and humorous complaints of their illnesses attributed to food and drink.

Some of the influential civilians in Washington, D.C., during the Civil War period—army contractors, politicians, office seekers, desk officers, etc., had a taste of food poisoning reported by Milton.[3] During both President Buchanan's and President Lincoln's administrations, hotels in the Capitol city, including the largest called "National Hotel" on Pennsylvania Avenue, established records for food poisoning outbreaks. The designation "National Hotel disease" became a byword and was attributed to "oversimplified kitchen sanitation."

U. S. Grant was a vegetarian in many respects, because he developed a hemophobia in his youth in his father's smelly tannery. He would, however, as the British military historian General J. F. C. Fuller stated, eat only beef that had been "cooked to a cinder," for the sight of blood or red meat completely destroyed his appetite. He often had only a sliced cucumber with vinegar and strong coffee for breakfast, as he had at 4:00 A.M., May 6, 1864, at the opening of the Battle of the Wilderness. At any rate, he was a light eater, and after all is said and done—a great general.

The plight of the Confederate soldiers during the last days of the Appomattox campaign was desperate in every way—a lost cause, starvation, dysentery, and nutritional depletion. The survivors were silent about eating mule and horse meat, but history records such rations. "The hardest ration was a kind of meat 'Nassau bacon' ('Nausea bacon') from the blockade runners made from tropical hogs and cured in sea brine . . . more likely discarded 'salt horse' or discarded ship's pork. It was

---

[3]Milton, G. F.: *Abraham Lincoln and The Fifth Column.* New York, Vangard Press, 1942.

discolored, scaly, spotted like pox, putrid, rancid, and utterly devoid of grease; elastic so it could be chewed like gum for a long time. Then by desperate effort you would gulp it down out of sight and hopefully out of mind . . . "[4] Poor quality of foods, both nutritionally and hygienically, was the rule in armies up to World War I. In both armies of the Civil War, pickled or heavily salted beef, known as "salt horse," met Washington and Richmond standards, namely, "Pickled beef must be salted so that the food does not decay for two years in the hottest climate." When leached of salt by the "cooks," it was always rancid, discolored, juiceless, and "really tough enough to resist a saber thrust."

Salt pork sides and backs, known as "sow belly," were always fat, rancid with aldehydes, flabby, and stringy. "The outsides were black as a shoe and the insides yellow with putrefaction." Reformers of the day cried out against "salt junk" as a producer of inordinate thirst for whiskey!

Hardtack (ship's "biscuit") was an old hard "cracker" of flour and water known for over four centuries as a durable food for ships' crews and armies.[5] These "bisquets" were always full of weevils or maggots, and thus appropriately called "worm castles." "Eat it in the dark of night so you can't tell whether or not it is inhabited." We were served the selfsame type of hardtack with weevil maggots at Plivot near Chalons-sur-Marne in World War I, the day before we fought in the battle of Blanc Mont Ridge and St. Etienne-a-Arnes.

The story of the rise of microbiology and eventual application of sanitary sciences and technologies to human needs provides a striking, contrasting picture with the past. Of course,

---

[4]Foote, Frank H.: *Southern Historical Society Papers*, Richmond, Vol. 31.

[5]Hardtack was in general use by soldiers, ships' crews, and pilgrims to the Holy Land before 1400 A.D. As an example, Roberto da Sanseverino, nephew of Duke Francesco Sforza of Milan, in his *Viaggo* (travels) to Palestine, Egypt, Syria, and Lebanon (1458 A.D.) tells how Arab raiders could often be bought off by presents of food, particularly hardtack, the pilgrim's staple food. He always looked forward to the more lush city areas where pilgrims would not have to chew hardtack with aching jaws.

the story is not ended, but enough has been accomplished to refute certain facets of criticisms weighed by H. J. Muller,[6] who wrote that certain critics say, "progress, a dubious concept in America, inspires a shameless boasting about a high standard of low living." Professor Muller contests this scorn by these critics of material progress. He advises them to recall the past and everyday life of most of the world's population.

---

[6]Muller, Herbert J.: *The Loom of History,* New York, Mentor Books, 1961, p. 82.

THE ROCKY MOUNTAIN MEN

ANOTHER FAMOUS GROUP, the Rocky Mountain men and plainsmen of the 1820's to 1860's whom our grandchildren know so well from TV, suffered grieviously on occasion from food poisoning. In scanning the voluminous literature now extant on Kit Carson, Jim Bridger, St. Vrain, Bill Williams, Fitzgerald, La Bonte, Cross Eagle, the Brents, Wyeth, and a host of others, including the French trappers from their old settlements on the Illinois and Mississippi Rivers, we find many allusions to sudden illness of this nature, aside from their many other dangers, told with grim and raucous humor, depending upon the teller or reporter.

For instance, in the summer of 1835, a party of Rocky Mountain trappers made up largely of French encamped for the day along a river in what is now the state of Idaho. They had been carrying (and incubating) their great delicacy, beaver tails, for their meal. "Meat is meat" was the slogan of the frontiersmen and mountain men. About two hours after eating the beaver tails which they thought tasted "slightly bisque," an explosive outbreak occurred—nausea, severe diarrhea, and vomiting (*Staphylococcus* enterointoxication). This inglorious state of being darkened their view of the beautiful valley and river, and so they named it "Malade River," or Sick River, which names have survived to this day.

The doughty mountain men appear not to have suffered chronic nutritional diseases at all during the decades of their sway, but tenderfeet often purged dreadfully from drinking alkali waters charged with magnesium sulfate and iron sulfates. We learn from records and hearsay that there were some bacterial food-poisoning outbreaks during warm weather, because their raw meats incubated when carried on the trail. The Rocky Mountain men did have their medical troubles, aside from venereal disease from squaws which we may infer from the tales

16

of Antoine Robidoux who, in the summer of 1840, returned to the Platte River country from the golden coast of California. "Why," said Robidoux, "fevers are so rare out yonder that when one man came down with the 'aigue,' neighbors came from a hundred miles around jes' to watch him shake."

An illness, once confused with "bad foods" by some writers, occurred in rarified atmosphere of great elevations. Before becoming adjusted to the thin air on high mountains for the first time, and exercising quite strenuously, mountain fever, characterized by splitting headaches, vomiting, nausea, and nervous depression, was frequently confused with "spoiled or bad foods." U. S. Grant suffered mountain sickness in Mexico which he described in his memoirs.

The Spanish Conquistadores, who in the sixteenth century invaded the lands of the Incas in the region of the Andes highlands and mountains, suffered grievously from altitude sickness. Their chronicles often refer to the soroche or "sickness of the Andes" (described by Father José de Acosta in his "Natural and Moral History" written in 1590.) "There is in Peru a high mountain called Pariacaca. When I rode up the 'stairs' on the top of this mountain, I was surprised with so mortal and strange pang that I almost fell off onto the ground. I vomited and retched and strained, casting up food, phlegm, yellow and green bile; in the end, blood and almost my soul. The thin air is the cause of altering the stomach, and trouble the complete disposition." Perhaps so. We formerly observed air-sickness of some individuals in the nonpressurized passenger aircraft of the 1920's and 1930's.

The Englishman, William Wey, in his *Itineraries* (1458 A.D.), gave much good advice to pilgrims to the Holy Land. Wey described one observation on both man and beast visiting the desolate waste of the Mount of Temptation, "Hyt ys passyng hot and ryght hye, when ye come downe a yen for nothyng drynke no water, but rest yow a lytyl, and then ette brede and drynke clene wyne w'oute water; after that grete heat water generyth a grete fluxe, other a fever, other bothe, than a man may haply lose hys lyfe thereby." These maladies also were seen in the dry, mountainous southwest of our nation in pioneer days. The etiology or etiologies are not clear today.

Francis Parkman, the great historian, when a young man, spent a few months in 1846 in the mountainous areas back of old Fort Laramie, usually with the Ogallala Sioux. He suffered greatly from severe diarrheas and weakness, which his biographer attributed to "colitis of neurogenic origin." Others now think his acute condition was aggravated by altitude, alkali water, and insanitary buffalo meat. That same year, Joel Palmer gave written advice to emigrants bound for Oregon, mentioning, "It is seldom, however, that emigrants are sick; but sometimes eating too freely of fresh buffalo meat causes diarrhea and sickness, and unless it be checked, soon prostrates the individual and leaves him a fit subject for chronic disease." (Buffalo are *Salmonella* carriers.)

Later, cholera outbreaks along the Oregon Trail in 1849, 1850, and 1852 took heavy toll. In 1830, a cholera carrier, or a light case in a Muslim pilgrim from Mecca, carried the disease to Europe. It spread by 1832 and appeared in American ports, especially New Orleans. By 1833 it moved up the river stations and to western trails. In Europe, a second epidemic occurred in 1847 to 1848, and following the wave of emigration to the United States of America, the cholera vibrios were carried to the Middle West. Fleeing to the West, California, and Oregon, emigrants carried the disease with them, contaminating the whole Oregon Trail. Many thousands of deaths occurred, and graves were to be seen for many years afterward all along the ribbons or "traces" of the great trail. Almost 50 per cent of the northern Cheyennes died from these cholera infections.

Treatments of infectious diseases were obviously not specific, and some of the physicians in the West were well-meaning but helpless. A case in point was the California Medical Association (1844-1846) comprised of three men, all without benefit of the Hippocratic Oath—John Marsh, Joe Meek, and G. M. Wasewitz. History relates that they were "high priced," and we hope they did not speed too many patients to their graves. Many weird tales, if not patients, survived their "practice." Calomel, theriac, whiskey, and laudanum in heroic doses were the cure-alls during those times in the Wild West. In contrast, consider the almost miraculous advances in the practices of medicine and surgery of today!

One of the memorable events of the Wild West, and the whole continent for that matter, was the great meteoric shower of November 12, 1833, which provided Jim Bridger and the other mountain men with tall tales for American tenderfeet. On this night, a dazzling shower of meteors blazed across the night sky. All America saw them, and everyone was deeply impressed—as impressed as their knowledge, emotions, religion, and awareness permitted them. Indians, Mormons, frontiersmen of all sorts, and all the categories that made up America never forgot the celestial blazes, and they long remembered "the night the stars fell" or "the night heaven cracked open and dripped fire, and the stars came tumbling down."

By some process known only to folklorists, Bridger, Black Mose Harris, and other Rocky Mountain trappers confused fossils, petrified trees, and various forms of decaying organic life with the heavenly display. The word "petrified" transmuted to "putrefied" and then to "spoiled." "Even the sun and moon thereafter shone with putrefied light." Harris told a St. Louis lady about the "putrefied" forests and all kinds of small and large animal fossils. "Did these things smell badly?" she asked. "Smell badly, Marm!" cried Harris, "Would a skunk stink ef he was froze to stone?" It is alleged that a minor controversy between zoologists and paleontologists of this period was neatly answered, "If the lifelike object stinks it belongs to the zoologist; if it does not, it (fossil) belongs to the paleontologist." At any rate, putrefaction, spoilage, and bowel troubles were hooked up somehow with the night the stars "fell."

We all know that spoiled and even putrefied meat and foods, do not necessarily cause food poisoning. There is a voluminous scientific literature now to prove this, founded on human-volunteer feeding tests. (We can if we wish, eat Limburger and "ripened" cheeses with impunity.) All of the Plains Indians ate tainted buffalo meat when they were forced to do so during deep-snow winters or when the animals were hard to find. Blackfeet Indians, Nez Perces, Cheyennes, Mandans, and Siouxans, under stress, are known to have eaten putrefied buffalo, drowned while crossing river ice and fetched ashore weeks later. No food poisoning resulted. There are many instances of this, especially during spring floods on the Missouri River when large numbers of dead buffalo, frozen in the ice floes, came down the current and were caught on sand bars or on shore impediments. The flesh was often green in tinge, but we know this entity is not, of itself, poisonous. (It is red myoglobin of the muscle oxidized to green choleglobin by oxidizing microorganisms and atmospheric oxygen.)[7]

One of Jim Bridger's tall tales which he loved to tell had it that at Salt Lake, which he discovered in the winter of 1830, it "snowed for seventy days. All the buffalo died, but were preserved frozen stiff in the snow. When spring came, all I had to do was to roll 'em into the Salt Lake and me and the Utes had pickled buffalo for years. Better 'n any salt hog you ever et going down, but a couple of hours after eating, left me and the Ute Injuns jes' as fast!"

Dr. Martin Petersen of the U. S. Army Quartermasters Laboratories has called our attention to another cause of intestinal distress among the white frontiersmen and horse soldiers of the Rockies. When the intelligent Mountain tribes were being pursued, they adulterated the water holes and springs with massive doses of a powdery substance which had been prepared from the dried bark of the cascara buckthorn. After the thirsty men had drunk deeply from the cold and limpid waters of these pristine springs and pools, they soon found themselves in the throes of stomach cramps and violent purging. Their digestive disturbance was so profound that pursuit was slowed to a grinding and groaning halt. One might consider this an early example of successful, even if undignified, chemical warfare.[8] While this distress was not bacteriologic in origin, the

---

[7] Jensen, L. B.: *Microbiology of Meats*. 3rd ed. Champaign, Garrard Press, 1954, Chap. 3.

sufferers would scarcely have been interested in a different diagnosis!

There was one peculiar type of bowel distress observed and talked about by all westerners during the "buffalo days." This condition, so common to inexperienced individuals in the West, was always ascribed to eating buffalo meat. It is now known that some of these illnesses were caused possibly by lack of fat in the diet, or frank bacterial food poisoning. The Indians themselves knew and practiced the rule that fat be included whenever possible. They drank bison kidney fat, but knew that soft, oily, belly fat, if taken too liberally, induced vomiting. They also loved bone-marrow fat. The French and American trappers avoided the "mal-de-vache" experienced by greenhorns by rigidly adhering to the Indian practice. There is also a long history of "dysenteries" following exclusive lean-meat dietaries, especially after eating horse meat (hippophagy) which we have discussed elsewhere.[9] Nathaniel Wyeth documents this in the case of the northern Rocky Mountain tribes who would not eat horse, but the Navajo had no objection to horse stew. General (then Captain) Fremont and a companion, Lt. A. H. Gillespie USMC, in 1846, made their way down the Sacramento valley, reaching camp at Lassen's rancho. They were very sick from a diet of horse meat but recovered rapidly on conventional foods provided by Mr. Lassen. It has been long known by explorers that the addition of carbohydrates and any palatable fat obviates this difficulty arising from an exclusive

---

[8] Ancient Greeks, on occasion, also practiced "intestinal warfare." Frontinus, the Roman general and famous engineer in charge of Roman aqueducts, tells us in his *Stratagems* (3.7.6) that Clisthenes in 201 B.C., besieging a Greek City, cut the water conduits for a period to cause great thirst. After turning on the water, now poisoned with hellebore, the inhabitants drinking the treated water were so weakened by diarrhea that they were easily overcome. Solon, Eurylochus, and other Greek leaders also employed this "stratagem" in sieges. Theophrastus (370-285 B.C.) described varieties of hellebores and purging properties at length as did Pausanias (Bk. X. 34. 7-8) and other ancient writers.

[9] Jensen, L. B.: *Man's Foods: Nutrition and Environments in Food Gathering Times and Food Producing Times.* Champaign, Garrard Press, 1953, p. 23, 103-104.

lean-meat diet. British Army Medical officers observed these effects when their troops were fed horse meat during the Mesopotamian campaign in World War I.[9]

Pemmican made exclusively of lean meat has a melancholy history both from growth of toxicogenic staphylococci, pathogenic enteric bacteria, and lack of nutritional balance. This has been known to bacteriologists and adequately proven to certain detachments of World War II soldiers who participated in a pemmican test; marching blithely out in the morning and returning to their New England camp in ambulances, jettisoning the pemmican both fore and aft. The "designer" of this pemmican had begun his academic career as a physical anthropologist at Harvard and extended his activities to Arctic exploration. Needless to say, the U.S. Army authorities asked him to direct his nutritional and culinary science to armies of the enemy.

E. N. Horsford, a Harvard professor, in 1863 had concocted this same meat ration, which he claimed would save the Union government $10,000,000 a year. It was tried out in Union regiments in Texas during that spring with disastrous results, felling every soldier who ate it (under compulsion, of course!). History repeats itself.

Indian-prepared pemmican did possess merit, both from a nutritional and perhaps hygienic standpoint, but only hardy stomachs and sharp teeth could deal successfully with it.

THE PASSENGER PIGEONS AND DISEASE[10]

W HEN WE WERE CHILDREN, many of the old timers told us of the passenger doves which they collected in great numbers. One of the tantalizing mysteries of Nature—tantalizing probably from the delights of obscurity—is the complete extinction of the passenger pigeon once so numerous in the New World. Crevecoeur, the writer of the "American Farmer" classic (1782), described the wild pigeon flights of twice a year as "numbers so astonishing as to obscure the sun in their flight." The last of these birds were a pair kept as caged pets in the 1870's in Ohio, and one of the rare taxidermist's specimens is now in the National Museum of Washington, D.C. Mathew Carey's "*Record of Malignant Fever*" (Philadelphia, 1793) and Longfellow's *Evangeline* saw a nexus of these birds and epidemics. Carey's statement is interesting: "Among the country people, large quantities of wild pigeons in the spring are regarded as certain indications of an unhealthy summer . . ." In *Evangeline*, Longfellow describes how,

> A pestilence fell on the city
> Presaged by wonderous signs, and mostly by flocks
>   of wild pigeons,
> Darkening the sun in their flight, with naught in
>   their claws but an acorn.

To the bacteriologist and virologist nowadays, two possibilities are suggestive of the great extinction and the epidemics and epizootics. *Salmonella*, one or more of a thousand serotypes, are commonly carried by all Aves, as well as by all vertebrate

---

[10]A complete history of the passenger pigeons can be found in C. W. Townsend's Chapter, pp. 379-402, in Bent, A. C.: *Life Histories of North American Gallinaceous Birds*. New York, Dover, 1963. (Townsend logically implicates indiscriminate wholesale slaughter and loss of breeding and nesting grounds as causes of extinction.

animals including reptiles. When any species population falls away from equilibrium and increase, many agencies inimical for survival tend in a short time to lead to extinction of that species.

Viruses of many types can now be isolated from domesticated birds (turkeys, ducks, geese, chickens, guinea fowl, pigeons), as well as most free birds of many genera. The Psittacine family of birds are not the only carriers of viruses as we know from more recent mosquito-borne outbreaks of encephalitis manifested by a variety of symptoms in infected humans in Texas and Florida. An outbreak in point was that of the St. Louis-type epidemic of the middle 1930's. (Equine encephalitis vectors were known at this time.) Personal observations documented by questionnaires of individual cases brought to light gastrointestinal symptoms severe enough to establish a false diagnosis of food poisoning. Many of the patients, upon recovery, brought law suits against retailers of foods, and usually purveyors were impleaded. Many defendants settled out of court, but those purveyors whose motto was "millions for defense; not one cent for tribute" and who knew the true nature of the epidemic battled it out in civil jury trials of cases with some verdicts for the defendant companies. One of the series of cases in which we served as a defendant witness for a retailer (a large chain-store corporation) presented to the court and jurors a many-faceted situation. The first case of this trial, based upon implied warranty, was led off by a Madame of an "establishment of easy virtue" who alleged that she and five of her pretty girls had suffered food poisoning from a designated peccant food. As the testimony moved on with clarifying cross-examination of the witnesses for the plaintiffs and factual evidence of the defendants based upon private investigations and U.S. Public Health Service data of the epidemic, as well as city and state public health data, the weight of the evidence, if not the preponderance of the testimony, left the jury with no alternative but to find for the defendant companies. (The elected judge denied a directed verdict, which is normal procedure in many communities.) Reporters of the daily press, catching on to our testimony of the passenger pigeons, ordinary pigeons, and bird vectors of these viral epidemics, added another adjective for the birds, "soiled doves."

SOME BIZARRE VIEWS OF FOODS
IN THE PAST

ASIDE FROM THE nutritional aspects of the *four basic classes* of foods (which have obviously been of prime importance in the history of mankind), there have been many misadventures with foods recorded in historical time and also in prehistory, judging from the many food taboos, rituals, and other sociologic manifestations associated with foods through the ages. As an example of the great boon of proper nutrition in buoyant health and mental vigor, we need only to recall Mark Twain's attitude towards the theories involving psychosomatic influences or virtues alleged to be transmitted to the consumer through eating certain foods. A young poet who was both ambitious and aggressive, but whose poems did not seem to catch on with the *literati*, accosted the always genial and helpful Mark Twain with, "Mr. Twain, my muse is suffering from some lack. Louis Agassiz, the great scientist, says that there is much phosphorus in fish and also in the brain. If I eat enough fish will this aid me with my creative work?" Mark removed the cigar from his mouth and lowering his great gray head, whispered to the youth, "Yes, it is true that Professor Agassiz has so said. Now, in your case I would suggest a couple of middlin' sized whales for the present—not the largest kind." Many years ago, we innocently remarked in one of our books, "Obviously no one will eat his way into the kingdom of Heaven, but behavior patterns appear to be influenced by good and bad nutrition." The European press quoted this widely as *ober dicta*.

When we study the history of the unwanted aspects of foods in past eras, we never are on safe scientific grounds before the rise of microbiology and chemistry, but we shall venture into this realm, citing a few episodes of food poisoning and food spoilage which illustrate unstressed historical material.

Some of our conjectures might place us in the category of a prophet, by a definition adapted from a humorous Hebrew saying: "When you get a paddling, you become a prophet for the simple reason that although you lie face down, you know pretty well what is going on above." Throughout recorded time, spoiled foods[11] in all manifestations were associated with food poisoning, but after the ptomaine theory was exploded (reluctantly in some circles), the picture became clear to everyone who cared to inquire. Cultural customs involving foods of all peoples of the planet varied greatly with environments—the Eskimos loved rotten fish, the old English squires demanded their game birds be hung for ripening, the Chinese loved pidan (putrefied eggs), peoples of the western nations still eat strong cheeses, and so on for an extended list.

The records surviving from the ancient Near East (today the Arabian-Muslim world), Greece, Rome, and medieval times are comparatively replete, sometimes by inference, in mentioning food troubles.

The ancient Egyptian baker was plagued with ropy bread, as was his medieval counterpart in Europe—the rope or slime in the interior of the loaf being a result of the growth of several members of the genus *Bacillus*. In London of the thirteenth century, the baker who sold ropy bread (innocently to be sure) was often punished by having his loaves tied around his neck and then flogged through the streets. According to modern philosophies, especially Kierkegaard's existentialist school, mental stresses produced in this way and other ways stimulate higher levels of cognition, i.e., deeper thinking. This may be a facetious outlook, but a few of these early bakers learned that if one pint of vinegar was added to one hundred pounds of flour, the entity disappeared from their bakeshops.

It is commonplace knowledge that chromogenic bacteria, notably *Serratia marcescens* (*Monas prodigiosa*) with its red pigment in bread, porridges, polenta, and the like caused con-

---

[11] Jensen, L. B.: *Meat and Meat Foods.* Humanizing Science Series. New York, Ronald Press, 1949, p. 188.

sternation with its bloody inferences. We recall that Dr. and Mrs. Robert Breed described in the *Journal of Bacteriology* the high mortality rate of people associated with bleeding bread and the great number of deaths resulting from executions on charges of witchcraft and impiety rather than the rarely pathogenic nature of this species.

The history of protein foods, with which we were most familiar, provides many examples of food acceptance or rejection. Dry sausages like salami, invented in the city of Salamis (now a deserted sandy waste) on the Isle of Cyprus, in quite early Phoenician and Greek times depended upon the omnipresent lactobacilli (producing the antiseptic lactic acid from muscle sugar (glycogen) during the drying process). Homer mentions sausages, and Aristophanes complained that Athenian sausagemakers used dog and donkey meat too liberally in their product. The Romans also developed many formulae for sausages, and it furnished a durable ration for the Legions together with bread, cheeses, salt, oil, and wine or "posca." Roman market police in many reigns kept food establishments in good order for those times and *botuli* or sausages which they condemned because of spoilage or green discolorations were thrown into the Tiber River.

The records of medieval Paris provide us with a sermon of the time of St. Louis the Crusader. "An old customer of a butcher of Paris asked to have his sausages cheaper, as he had dealt only with the one *charcutier* (sausagemaker) for seven years." "Seven years," cried the charcutier in astonishment, "and you are still alive?"

Langland, in *Piers Plowman* (1375 A.D.), a good reporter of his times, wrote:

> To punish on pillories
> And punishment stooles
> Brewers and Bakers
> Bochiers and Cookes
> For these are men on this molde
> That moost harm worketh
> To the poor people.

In the year 1319, the meat-inspection wardens of London apprehended one William Sperling selling putrid and poisonous meat by candlelight. Sperling was whipped, placed on a stool of punishment, and the offending foods were burned beneath him—the smoke and stench being regarded as purifying agents.

Leprosy of ancient and medieval times (the clinical entity was sadly confused with many chronic skin diseases) was thought to result from eating spoiled meat and fish. In the Oxford Agreement of 1356, the city of Oxford formally granted the chancellor of the University of Oxford jurisdiction over the meat and fish markets "and over all foods that shall be found to be putrid, unclean, vicious, or otherwise unfit on this condition: that the foods forfeited be given to the leper hospital of St. John." Thirty years later, the Scottish Parliament enacted the same law, stating that the "poor leper-folk be given spoiled meat and fish and moldy grain." Since leprosy had been "caused" by such foods, spoiled meats and grains could not harm the poor leper-folk. By early spring in northern and western Europe, the records show that much of the foods were in various states of spoilage, and that spices and savoring herbs were in great demand.

SPECIFIC HISTORICAL CASES

There is a comparatively large literature on St. Paul the Apostle's health. St. Paul suffered serious illness in the year 50 A.D. on the occasion of his preaching among the Galatians, those invading Gauls and distant brothers of the Irish, Welsh, Scots, and Bretons, who settled in Asia Minor in 235 B.C. Had he not become ill there, we might never have had his authentic Galatian letters. The cordial Galatians aided Paulist christianity in many wonderful ways. While students of religion and pathology have invoked many illnesses that Paul might have suffered when he was stricken on his travels (he had not intended to stop in Galatia), St. Thomas Aquinas says that Paul suffered *morbus iliacus* or intestinal disease, and we are content to be a Thomist in this diagnosis. Let doubting Thomists discover something other than shigellosis or salmonellosis. As we go further back in historical time to 401 B.C., we encounter Xenophon and the "Immortal 10,000" in their escape from the Persians, who nearly came to an ignoble end after reaching the Black Sea. They ate ravenously of the rhododendron-laurel poisonous honey, still causing trouble in Asia Minor (Turkey), and Xenophon in his *Anabasis* describes the dreary defeat from nature in detail.

Julius Caesar's legions in Gaul, according to Professor James Breasted and others, had their trouble with fresh meats, and this was long the fate of meat foods in European campaigns before efficient veterinary inspection and refrigerated transport. Traditionally, the Roman soldier's ration was a hard, dry one not subject to frank spoilage for a certain length of time. (We had our "C" rations.) Caesar favored olive oil, cheeses, and dry sausage. The Legionnaires' standard rations usually consisted of huge portions of coarse wheat bread, wheat porridge, available vegetables and fruits, cured smoked bacon (*durati sale terga suis*), cheeses, olive oil, and *posca* to drink. *Posca* was a cheap wine diluted with vinegar (fairly germicidal due to its acetic acid content). This issued beverage was highly esteemed by the soldiers. Bible students recall that *posca* was offered to Christ on the cross by the Roman soldier at the crucifixion. In the better Roman armies before the "decline and fall" of the Empire, a *medicus legionis,* who headed the medical staff, cared for the health of the troops. This military physician and surgeon was in charge of camp sanitation which was better understood then by the military than at any time up to World War I! Breasted pointed out that Julius Caesar's food logistics in his wars in Gaul, Spain, and the Near East were a deciding factor in his conquests. Caesar perceived that if he could feed his intact army for any length of time with decent food, he could overcome the Gauls *et al.*, who had not developed this phase of logistics and therefore must scatter in small units to obtain perishable food supplies and thus meet Roman onslaught with certain defeat. Epidemics in his army were of relatively rare occurrence compared to epidemics and pandemics in the civilian population. However, one of Caesar's legions suffered severe ergot poisoning from bread made with infected grain near Marseilles.

The later "bad" Roman emperors provided each Legion staff with a professional poisoner to head off "ambitious men, both Roman and barbarian." The poisoner's toxicologic kit contained dried soluble powdered mushrooms of four species, arsenic, and four lethal alkaloids including aconite.

Students of Roman military history and archaeology of Roman camps (both permanent and field) have shown the hygienic "layouts," especially in Gaul. The two bisecting main streets, drains, latrine facilities, food *samstellungs*, water supplies, camp infirmaries, and burial grounds all functioned well for hygiene. Naturally, strict discipline, far removed from the martinet impositions of a later time, made these things possible.

When we view the hygienic conditions prevalent in the Spanish-American War encampments in Tennessee, Florida, Cuba, and elsewhere, we note grimly the lack of progress and the forgotten military rules of Julius Caesar. These encampments were bereft of hygienic science and technology, judging from the appalling incidence of salmonellosis and shigellosis, usually typhoid and paratyphoid fevers. Unbelievably bad provisions, including beef and pork products preserved with formaldehyde, were fed these gallant volunteers. The "germ theory of disease" was known in that decade before the turn of the century, but obviously not applied, although some of the junior medical officers who possessed little or no authority tried to remedy this defective state of affairs. The present writer recalls that one of these junior medics said long afterwards, "Caesar's Legions were provided with better 'winter quarters' than evidenced in our volunteer army."

Two thousand years later on the same battle terrains of Caesar in Gaul (France) the Imperial German Army suffered a blow that Caesar's food logistics would have avoided. We recall the horrible World War I battles of Verdun (when the Germans tried desperately to take Verdun from the French, whose hero, General Petain, became immortalized until World War II) and Vichy. The German Army Corps' butchers had made a large amount of fresh sausage, a delicacy for their attacking commando troops. The butchers ate of it some two days before it was distributed, without any reactions except a longing to eat more. Then, about 3,000 of the best assault troops were fed this ration, and in two to three hours Verdun was saved from that assault. Nearly all at risk became violently ill with what we now know to be *Staphylococcus* intoxication, i.e. violent diarrhea, vomiting, retching and cramps, immobility, and thready pulse. It was a dreary, sticky mess. The lowly but potent *Staphylococcus* made a hero of General Petain who said, "They shall not pass," and shamed German militarism.[12] The Verdun military ribbon should show a cluster of S. *aureus* colored a bright golden yellow on a brown background. Thousands of such outbreaks caused by staphylococci occurred in World War I, and since bacteriologists had little or no voice but all the pertinent data to correct these poisonings in World War II, the busy little omnipresent coccus carried on its undignified role (and obviously dangerous role when armed men were awaiting combat or in combat). We have collected so many accounts of these outbreaks in World Wars I and II that we would be prolix to cite what all men involved know only too well. Suffice it to say that too many bomber training planes came down with all hands in the throws of this knockout condition; gun crews often lay in what might be called odoriferous positions around their clean cannons; company streets were often slippery. During the early stages of World War II, we recall visiting many training camps to investigate this mess, but the impression of one call still stays with me. One of the Naval Commandants of the Chicago Navy Pier, facetiously referred to as "U.S.S. Concrete," told me his command suffered *Staphylococcus* food poi-

---

[12]Baerthlein, K.: *Munchen. Med. Wschr. 69*:155, 1922. Staphylococcus food poisoning was unknown. The German medics attributed the outbreak to *Proteus vulgaris*. Staphylococci were found in the sausage but disregarded as the etiologic factor. Dr. M. A. Barber, a contract army physician in the Philippines, had proven by a human-volunteer test (himself) that staphylococci of a certain variety caused enterointoxication. This information lay buried in the Philippine *J. Sci. 9*:515-519, 1914.

soning. He also whispered to me "We must put a stop to this. I'm too damned near the Chicago Tribune Tower and (editor) Colonel McCormick for safety." Remedial measures were instituted and published for the Armed Forces.

An anecdote from the Napoleonic wars has long amused food bacteriologists. After Appert's method of glass packing and canning of foods achieved some degree of practicality in France of 1806, the great Donkin and Hall Iron Works in England began to can ("tinned cannisters") foods of all sorts, to provision warships, armies, and expeditions. There is a record of a letter from Spain, April 30, 1813, written by the clerk of the Duke of Wellington (he who vanquished Napoleon) to these canners saying that his lordship found the canned beef very good and added tactlessly that his lordship could not write at the present time owing to his being so much indisposed (with vomiting and diarrhea). Naturally, scientifically controlled canning procedures have eliminated these undignified and even lethal factors, especially when trained, apprehensive bacteriologists have a voice of command in the cannery.

STAPHYLOCOCCI

ALTHOUGH STAPHYLOCOCCI were not discovered until 1880 when Pasteur found them in pus and were not tentatively classified until 1884 by Rosenbach, inferences of illness from preformed toxin produced by them in foods can be found in medical treatises for over one hundred years. Not until 1930, when Dr. G. M. Dack[13,14] discovered *S. aureus* as the cause of widespread acute food intoxications was the "modern era" in this field opened up for extended researches. Dack proved the toxic nature of some *Staphylococcus* culture extracts, their physiology and epidemiology, their effects when ingested by man (symptomology), and the diagnosis and treatment of the patient. We have already mentioned the work of the contract surgeon, M. A. Barber, on *Staphylococcus* enterointoxication which lay buried in the Philippine Journal of Science since 1914. It was this year in July when the present writer, partaking of a mess-kit-full of militia noon rations in northwest Iowa experienced with other "dodgasted militiamen" (as the regular army called them) the humiliating seige and bitter sequelae of acute staphylococcal gastroenteritis. Company streets became slippery and suspenders a nuisance except when kept in a lowered position. The graphic description of *Staphylococcus* food poisoning written by Dolman[15] recalled to memory the syndrome of acute *Staphylococcus* enterointoxication in the encampment on that hot Iowa prairie so long ago. Dolman and colleagues had swallowed toxic *Staphylococcus* filtrates as "human volunteers." As

[13]Dack, G. M.: *Food Poisoning.* 3rd ed. Chicago, University of Chicago Press, pp. 109-159.

[14]Meyer, K. F.: 1956, Food poisoning. *New Engl. J. Med. 249*:765-812, 1953.

[15]Dolman, C. E.: Bacterial food poisoning. *Canad. J. Public Health, 34*:97-111 and 205-235, 1943.

others had observed in those days, ordinary laboratory test animals were not susceptible to the toxin *per os*. Only primates—man, and monkeys to a lesser extent— were susceptible. Dolman wrote:

> The vomiting is accompanied, and sometimes replaced, by considerable retching. At first, one is astonished to note from what depths and after what strivings it is possible to recall portions of meals long forgotten; but as the stomach empties of food, bile-stained, and even blood-flecked mucus becomes the chief return. Abdominal cramps and diarrhea are often very marked and may precede the vomiting but more usually begin after the vomiting has started and may continue after it has ceased. The first evacuation may be merely a loose stool, but this is apt to be followed by frequent and remarkably profuse discharges of watery fluid. The resulting dehydration no doubt accounts largely for the pinched, shocked appearance of the subjects and to some extent also for the marked lassitude and depression which sets in after the first glamour of a positive reaction has given way to disenchantment. The ordeal can perhaps be compared to pregnancy, in that it may have been lightheartedly enough embarked upon the first time but is not so willingly repeated, and in its being made bearable as the situation moves towards a climax, only by the reflection that deliverance is bound to come. Once begun, recovery was usually rapid, the only aftereffects being a large appetite, and a sense as of calm after a storm.

Over the years, clinicians or their laboratory men encountered *Staphylococcus* infections all too frequently, as they still do to this day. For many years before the rise of bacteriology, surgeons observing wounds and amputations (especially during the Civil War) noted that a prognosis of sorts could be made out from the character of pus. If the exudate was plentiful and creamy it was called "laudable pus" which, in after years, was found to be active phagocytic reactions usually elicited by staphylococci. The prognosis was considered good in these cases. Should little or no pus be formed and the amputated stump or wound appear cyanotic, the scanty exudate was termed "malignant pus of blood poisoning," later associated with *streptococcus* infections. These observations were useful but were far from being precise, since clinical microbiologists now know of many

other microorganisms singly or in mixed infections which com-
plicate this picture, notably the anaerobes, the scourge of battle
wounds in France of 1914-1918, with which we dealt morosely
and referred to the surgeons.

Since 1884, the pathogenic staphylococci of greater or less
virulence were found to be omnipresent in the environments of
man and animals. Hence, when found in great numbers in a
suspected or peccant food, these microorganisms were considered to be ordinary contaminants, as we have noted in the case
of the analysis of the heroic sausages that saved Verdun from
an assault in World War I. Having access to the old laboratory
reports on food examination filed in many public health offices,
academic, commercial, and army "archives" before 1930, we
often found this composite statement: "This specimen (naming
the food or foods submitted for analysis) harbored *Proteus*
bacilli, no typhoid bacilli, many *B. coli* and slow lactose fer-
menters, no *B. botulinus,* no paratyphoid or dysentery groups,
etc. Numerous *S. aureus* and other nonfood-poisoning types of
bacteria were found."

The ptomaine theory of food poisoning, first introduced by
Selmi in 1870, long held sway in many diagnoses as the etiologic
agent. The American Medical Association in the 1920's no
longer accepted the term as a valid clinical designation. Pto-
maines were neither a specific entity nor a recognizable group
of poisonous substances thought to be present in spoiled foods;
hence the term was unscientific and without meaning. We encountered the designation, however, in most of the states up
to 1940 as a cause of gastrointestinal illnesses. It was a catchall
category for those who had many other clinical entities to reckon
with. Recalling the sorry state of food analyses during the years
up to 1930, one should not "cast the first stone" at the devotees
of the time-honored but now meaningless ptomaine theory. A
sobering thought which occurs to humble but otherwise really
scientific workers who know the past arises from a dim vision
of the future when current theories established by authorities
in a field of inquiry will appear as unscientific as Selmi's *ptoma*
(Latin, corpse) extractives once did.

Laws are high-probability statements like, "If I eat a green apple, I will get sick." This can explain sickness in small boys who have probably been smoking tobacco or cornsilk, but this law, typical of all theories and laws of science and conduct, is a penance explanation of sickness. A theory, and a law for that matter, is work knitted together in one elegant idea based on an enormous collection of useless facts. Biology and physics are not tales told by idiots because no idiot is irrational enough to think up such tales. Microbiologists (except molecular biologists), at least, know that it is a profound error to believe that everything about their subject has been discovered; it is mistaking the horizon for the boundary.

Of the large number of known microbial genera and species, not many are capable of inducing food-borne illnesses in man. The genera most frequently found and readily proven to be involved are (1) *Staphylococcus*, (2) *Salmonella*, (3) *C. botulinum* types, (4) type D *Streptococcus*, (5) *C. perfringens*, (6) *B. cereus*, (7) paracolon groups, and (8) *Shigella* (not necessarily food borne). There are growing lists of microorganisms which may or may not cause food-borne illness when present in suspected foods in large numbers. Human-volunteer tests with *proteus* bacilli, *pseudomonas*, certain coliforms, etc., have not established clear-cut proof of being causal agents, but several viruses fed to volunteers do simulate classical symptoms of food poisoning.

Everyone in this area of practice and research sees too much of poisonings from certain fungi and green plants, poisonous shellfish and fish, chemical poisons in food and drink, together with inhalation of poisonous gases like methyl chloride and carbon monoxide, which may simulate symptoms of food poisoning.[16] With a rising population and concomitant increase in incidence of gastrointestinal disease (numerous Americans eat at least one meal each day away from home) the problems of prevention obviously grow more complex.

---

[16]Jensen, L. B.: *Food Poisoning. J. Forensic Sci.* 2:355-372, 1956. Reprinted by the U.S. Public Health Service.

During this past half-century, especially in our early years in the field, many of us felt downcast viewing the total picture, but we were never so helpless as the Sumerian milker. A cuneiform tablet from ancient Sumer in lower Mesopotamia written about 5,000 years ago during the dawn of civilization in that area carried the ancient milkers' complaint: "If the gods want people to have clean milk they should have placed the udders on the forepart of the cows!" These ancient milkers sat behind the cow to milk her, with the animal's tail over their left shoulders.

We were more progressive and certainly not stumped into inertia through reliance upon the vagaries of Marduk, the Near Eastern god, whom the ancient Greeks overthrew by means of dialectical scientific reasoning. This type of mental agility has guided Western civilization ever since, except perhaps during the wasted millennium of the Middle or Dark Age. (No doubt future ages will view the twentieth century as the Black or Gray Age.) Elderly scientists are not brash idealists for the reason stated by H. L. Mencken over forty-five years ago: "An idealist is one who, on noticing that a rose smells better than a cabbage, concludes it will also make better soup."

During the early 1930's, the controversies over the role of staphylococci in enterointoxication produced a minor paper blizzard of correspondence and articles, ranging widely in comments from haughty sniffs to downright sardonic laughter. Most Europeans and Americans interested in the field scouted this theory—and with some justification based on their laboratory researches. They found that not all staphylococci formed toxin. One really talented team of workers had grown these bacteria, both chromogenic and nonpigmented pure cultures, in broth, filtered the broth and swallowed the filtrates. No symptoms occurred even after repeated tests with many cultures. Thus this group requested a culture of *S. aureus* from the University of Chicago known by the Chicago group to be the "real McCoy." Nothing was heard following this request for several weeks when an explanatory letter arrived. Briefly, the group, upon receiving this culture, prepared the broth filtrates "as usual," swallowed some of it after lunch with confidence born of experience. As college professors often do, they "knocked off" about two hours after lunch (3:00 P.M.), and like all professors of those times they were too poor to own a car. Boarding a street car, they (two of them—the diener remained at toil) passed the municipal park. The season was late autumn. Hurriedly leaving the street car when nausea and foreboding cramps set in, they made for the bushes and trees which did not suitably screen them from view (no leaves!). Sitting on their haunches, but clothed in frock coat and striped pants of British make, the episode described so graphically by Dolman (previously cited) became a sticky, sickly reality. "The greatest humiliation suffered was brought about by some urchins playing in the park. . . These young ones surrounded us and played 'ring-around-the rosey'." . . "We heartily concur with your discovery of staphylococcus as formers of enterotoxin—no doubt about it!"

Increasing numbers of outbreaks of acute explosive food poisoning began to be noticed after 1930. This sharp increase in incidence was, of course, due to increased awareness of the role of enterotoxic staphylococci and also to the introduction of new processes in preparing various foods for retail marketing and consumption. From a handful of researchers busy with the problem of identifying toxin-formers, likely sources of food-poisoning types, suitable test animals susceptible to the toxins, and the nature of the poison, the number of experimenters grew in response to the seriousness of the situation until many of the facets of the problems were partially solved, at least. A good working knowledge and establishment of a fairly concise "Standard Method" was beginning to emerge from the vagaries of biologic data. Perhaps we should say from lack of statistical data which could not be had from the limited budgets for research, now a dim memory in these days of Federal billions for inquiries. (*"Research"* is a bad name, even when the second syllable is correctly accented and is used by columnists and editorial writers who gleefully point out "Federal grants-in-aid for projects on the forty-ninth right hind leg of a centipede.") It is gratifying to see scientists showered with support, although many of them are individually neglected. Scientists, like other people, bleed when they are pricked. And when scientists in the food-poisoning field fall victim of enterointoxication or intestinal infections, upon recovery from the bout, they are as mad about it all as a bridegroom we once met during a trial of a case in which we served as an expert witness. His wedding party, typical of Eastern European custom, in a small town in a coal-mining district, was held at the town-hall dance floor. Ham sandwiches from five large hams cooked and then incubated four days at 82° F. ± 5°, as well as other foods, were served there. Those who were to dance with the bride were also expected to deposit "folding money" in a barrel placed in the center of the dance floor. Food and beer were partaken from two to three hours prior to the dance. The incubation period for onset of staphylococcus food poisoning is 1.5 to 4 hours (median, 2.5 hours). Charitably, we must describe the event as a messy sadness. The bride was befouled and so were the many guests. "There was no dancing but much prancing," said a witness. No money was deposited in the barrel. Only the bridegroom, too busy with details to eat, escaped, whereupon he brought suit against processors and retailer based on the theory of implied warranty for $20,000 *ad damnum* setting forth as one item for recovery of moneys or compensation, "loss of bride's services for ten days." The kindly old judge remarked in an aside: "It is obvious to this court that the plaintiff in this case is a very young man!" We gleaned little information about the mood of the bride, but we shall always wish her well.

ENTEROTOXIC STAPHYLOCOCCI AND "MONKEY BUSINESS"

Since staphylococci are omnipresent in Nature, their presence has long been known through simple cultural isolations. Their stained appearance, i.e. round cells in bunches or grapelike clusters made for easy identification. One of our old German-American professors delighted us young students by declaring that, "der staphylokokken, dey comes in punches!" Semantically, Herr Professor Doktor von Vebber was close to the mark.

Until methods of testing for toxigenicity of a given strain of *S. aureus, S. albus, S. roseus, S. citreus et al.,* were at hand, human volunteers were the test subjects. Barnum of circus fame was wrong when he declared, "There's a sucker born every minute." Most volunteers volunteered only once, thank you! No repeat tests. But some investigators stayed with the problem, naturally partaking of *very small* doses only. Monkeys became the standard test animals, but they were far less susceptible than most humans. We encountered a few adult *Macaca mulatta* (rhesus monkey) and *M. irus* (Cynomolgus) monkeys that required heroic doses of known toxic filtrates to make them ill with vomiting and diarrhea. All other laboratory animals and domestic animals "drank" the toxic filtrate with impunity.

Our own colonies of rhesus monkeys were supplied to me in 1930 by a New York importer of exotic animals. These "naughty amoral beasties"—six males and six females in a colony—"were a caution," as the old maid said. One of the males appeared to be the boss. From fighting or sin, one of his eyelids hung down (ptosis) and he appeared truculent, possessive, battle-scarred, and treacherous. We called him Jonas. When force-fed a toxic filtrate, he objected strenuously, and when the toxic effects—presumably nausea and cramping—began, Jonas backed up to a corner of the cage, sitting on his tail, and scowled at humans. Placing his paws over his belly like an alderman, he would burp a little and vomitus coming up was retained in his "cheek pouches." Swallowing this material after several such events (Jonas apparently being a greedy monkey would not discard, like the Scots' saying about church offerings, "in for once, in for aye"), he would finally jettison the vomitus in a rainbow trajectory and give in to toxicology without more ado.

We made a bad mistake keeping our menagerie in a large cage. When reaching in to grasp a monkey with human arms and hands protected with heavy leather against sharp teeth, the wily beasts, when seized, would let fly with unerring aim causing us to become defiled and to reek like an unkempt zoological garden.

One of the males remained a runt—never grew up—and was

playful and decent. We called it Pavlov after the great Russian physiologist and psychologist. The colony was first tested for susceptibility to the enterotoxin by force-feeding with a stomach tube approximately 35 ml. of standard toxic filtrate (which will be described later). Little Pavlov was never tested, but given monkey delicacies to eat. When the test monkeys were in the throes of enterointoxication, Pavlov also tried to vomit and occasionally succeeded in regurgitating a little of his food into his cheek pouches. He never could effect diarrhea, but stubbornly persisted in straining at the job. This monkey reminds one of some people in institutional and Armed Forces feeding when an unreasoning person will loudly allege illness from the foods and soon many are experiencing little Pavlov's reaction.

There has been so much monkey business in the field of food-borne illness—especially when those who suffered illnesses resembling food poisoning or frank cases have resorted to the courts for damages—that some additional fleeting glances at monkeys may not be a digression. Together with colleagues in Chicago and elsewhere, we have either owned or had access to monkey colonies in the laboratories for over forty years. We also experimented with chimpanzees when we were on the staff of Mayo Clinic and Foundation. Since man is also a primate, the monkeys and apes are obviously much needed in a variety of medical researches. As was brought out in 1950 during some official hearings on toxicology in Washington, D. C., the lower animals, especially albino rats and mice, dogs, guinea pigs, rabbits, ferrets, hamsters, etc. do not react as man to materials under investigation such as food additives (and microbial poisons). Our own experiments over the years showed that botulinum toxins A and B were not very toxic for mink, but type C toxin was phenomonally lethal. Swine could drink millions of toxic units of botulinum toxins A and B with impunity but sickened and died after eating a few green cockleburrs! While rodents do not have active vomiting centers, cats and kittens do; hence injections of staphylococcal toxic filtrates were recommended by some investigators for identification of toxigenic strains of these bacteria. However, other investigators, including our group, observed that uninoculated plain nutrient broth, when injected intraperitoneally into cats and kittens, induced vomiting. Young pigs also reacted like the felines to injection. This left us with the alternative of monkeys or man. Man ordinarily stepped aside and the monkeys performed above and beyond the call of duty. In recent years the Government of India, representing peoples believing in transmigration of souls, held that "monkeys is people" as Bugs Baer said so often, and refused to ship us monkeys unless the "citizens" were used for absolutely critical experiments. Well and good! Our colonies were not mistreated, and we learned much from these little rhesus rascals aside from their dexterity in amoral activities. Perhaps one lesson in pedagogy or educational psychology should be cited. A confirmed bachelor trained a less-boisterous young rhesus monkey to be his house pet. The little pet was hard to housebreak and each time it defiled the sofa and easy chair of its master by defecation, our friend would pick it up, raise its tail, spank it soundly and throw it out of a window. One day the monkey defiled the sofa, reached back, slapped its own hind end and dutifully jumped out of the window! At any rate, the training or teaching method was conventional, but the pupil (like many of his distant human relatives) interpreted the impact of flagellating hands with up-to-date Gestalt psychology and Dewey pedagogy.

Another object lesson for us humans can be had from the ancient method of capturing monkeys without injuring them. A small hole is drilled into a gourd or coconut shell and rice grains placed therein. The aperture is just big enough for the monkey to work his greedy little hand into the rice or other monkey delicacies inside the trap. Holding a handful of grains, the avaricious fellow forms a fist which cannot be withdrawn through the hole. He never lets go and thus is easily captured. This is a lesson easily applicable to man! As Goldsmith wrote about one of his characters, "Tho' defeated, he could argue still."

For both scientific and medicolegal purposes, a strain of staphylococci must be identified as toxigenic or atoxic. Serological-biochemical *in vitro* methods[17] were under study, but until such methods provided valid data, the monkey-feeding test was preferable for court and jury purposes as well as for the exacting demands of the epidemiologist. The bacteriophage method of typing these bacteria is certainly very useful for tracing a strain to its lair. For unequivocal legal data, the toxin should be identified. The monkey species are rather finicky about holding down emulsified force-fed peccant foods under investigation and usually regurgitate the emulsions. Preformed enterotoxin in foods like meats of all kinds, ice cream mixes, cheeses, and a long list of human comestibles are not easily detected by current methods except, of course, when harboring millions of viable staphylococci (which can be tested by monkey feeding). Culinary heat-killed coccal cells can be estimated from quantitative stained-smear methods and evidence adduced as to presence of preformed toxin, but human volunteers partaking of graded "doses" of the suspected food clinch the argument. No wonder food companies have spent large sums of money for research on this problem with the objective of valid *in vitro* tests to demonstrate enterotoxin in any vehicle— food, culture media, or dejecta.

Since 1931, we have fed (by stomach tube) numerous monkeys with various broth cultures of suspected toxigenic staphylococci. The test monkeys, when force fed 50 to 60 ml each of special broth incubated with 20% CO_2 at 37° C for 48 hours, will, if enterotoxin is present, vomit (with diarrhea in some instances) in one to four hours, usually two to three hours. This test correlates with human-volunteer tests with the notable exception of dosage. Monkeys are far less susceptible than humans but were the only available animals which reacted to staphylococcal enterotoxin. Both man and monkeys establish some immunity after repeated tests, so a monkey suffering five bouts was discarded as a test subject for medicolegal reasons.

---

[17]Serological tests are now perfected by Dack and Bergdoll (1967) of The University of Chicago and are in general use.

Many years ago Dolman, for research purposes, prepared the toxoid employing the conventional formalin procedure, which protected humans from the food poison in lesser amounts of ingested peccant food. With one notable exception in human volunteers numbering about 250 persons, all were susceptible to the toxin. In spontaneous outbreaks involving large numbers at risk, one or several people appear to escape with mild symptoms or none at all! Ordinarily, the bigger the meal the more bitter the misery. We recall one case described by Davis[18] as an illustration to the point. He wrote that in 1926, Charles Lindbergh, while flying the United States Mail, ate one evening in a St. Louis restaurant and coming back to his room experienced an almost disastrous seige of food poisoning. His fellow roomers thought he would die, but he refused medical attention. His fellow fliers well knew that if tainted food were placed before him in those days when he was an impressive trencherman, his dose of poison would be dangerously large.

Staphylococci, when growing in meats or other foods, do not form any products detectable by smell, taste, or appearance; hence Davis is wrong about "tainted food" (organoleptic defects) and a nexus with food poisoning. Of the bacterial food poisoners, only *C. botulinum* may cause some "butyric" or putrefactive changes, but in botulinum intoxication there is ordinarily no vomiting, constipation is usually observed, and ascending paralysis from the neurotoxin effects a different train of sequelae leading to death from respiratory failure in 65 to 80 per cent of those stricken. Charles Lindbergh suffered staphylococcal food poisoning in 1926.

Based upon over fifty years of work in the areas of microbiology, pathology, forensic sciences, epidemiology, and food technology, we have arrived at some firm conclusions in the total field. On the other hand, during the decades engaged in this turbulent work, we on occasion (for a few hours usually) became a disintegrating raft on a chaotic sea. We said in a lec-

---

[18]Davis, Kenneth S.: *The Hero.* New York, Doubleday, 1959, p. 135.

ture at the War Conference (1943) on Army feeding[19] when concluding the talk:

> It is difficult to determine the value of many methods which are not time-tried, and we are ever reminded of the preparation of the ancient Damascus sword steel. Old travellers and the crusaders, Palgrave tells us, saw how the matchless Damascus steel was prepared by burying worn-out horseshoes in damp cellars. The metal's weaker portions perished slowly by oxidation, and the bright particles (alloys) were discovered shining midst the brown rust and in them was concentrated the essence of the trenchant ore. This Arabian process typifies much of human endeavor, and while much 'rusting' is likely to occur as time modifies our methods, there are always remaining some shining trenchant particles of useful information.

The enterotoxic staphylococci may be chromogenic or non-pigmented, but *S. aureus*, golden, yellowish, and orange varieties, are the usual offenders. Dr. Barber's original strain was white (albus) and we have encountered about fifty strains of nonpigmented staphylococci which were potent toxin formers. Chromogenesis is not at all a certain criterion of toxigenicity nor is hemolysis. The chemical configurations of pigments are now well known. So too is the genetic nature of bacteria. In 1931, 1941, and 1947 we personally encountered red pigmented forms appearing in apparently pure lines of *S. aureus* of known toxigenicity. These red strains had been called *S. roseus*.[20] In one episode in New Mexico (1941), a red strain of toxic staphylococcus was isolated from a prepared food having caused death of two elderly persons. These three enterotoxic red pigmented strains were not accepted as valid food poisoners by certain groups in our field. Although the doubters had free access to our cultures and data, they let the matter drop. Evidently they felt as Albert Einstein did when he commented after reading a fellow scientist's treatise: "I enjoyed the data but I didn't read

---

[19]Jensen, L. B.: Prevention of bacterial food poisoning by food preserving methods. *J. Amer. Vet. Med. Ass.* CIV:63-65, 1944.

[20]Pinner, M., and Voldrich, M.: Derivation of *Staphylococcus albus, citreus,* and *roseus* from *Staphylococcus aureus. J. Infect. Dis., 50*:185-202. 1932.

the novel." Naturally, any finding out of the ordinary excites criticism, as well it should, for confirmation and validity. When one "sticks his head and neck out of his carapace," there are verbal sticks and stones to cause him to withdraw into his shell.

The coagulase test was not a criterion which could be used in forensic and court cases, although some laboratory people placed great reliance on it. In an extended cheddar cheese survey, we isolated staphylococci of all varieties, some coagulase-positive and some -negative. Human volunteer and standard monkey-feeding tests did not correlate toxicity with coagulase. A competitor in the field who was "bucking for sergeant" wrote a rebuke of our findings and got his stripes.

In plating dilutions of the suspected peccant foods, the best medium for the purpose, we thought, was one devised by the British worker, Ludlum. This medium masqueraded under a variety of workers names,[21] but now is called tellurite glycine agar. (Apply dilutions by smearing with a sterile bent glass rod.) Black colonies are likely colonies for the monkey broth-feeding tests. When suspected foods are retrieved from the garbage pail (as health officers must often do) serial dilutions in 7.5% salt (NaCl) beef heart tubes are useful in suppressing gross contamination upon incubation. Staphylococci grow in high concentrations of salt.

During World War II, we were sent to Havana and Oriente Province, Cuba, to evaluate and judge a huge amount of salted beef collected there as reserve protein for the Cuban people owing to German wolf-pack submarines sinking many food-cargo ships. This beef, cured in 100° salometer salt brine (and nitrate added) was placed in tierces and before heading up, shovels full of salt were added. Storage was faulty, since the wooden tierces were only under sun cover and held openly at 82 to 92° F for nine months, without wetting down the barrels. The meat thus held was rancid in taste and dangerous when we

---

[21]A great deal of *borrowing* goes on in scientific circles, thus eliminating the need for the generous acts of *lending!*

found myriads of staphylococci per gram of meat. Some cultures were toxic, others atoxic. What to do? It was government property. At long last we hired boats to take the casks far out to sea, unheaded them and jettisoned the whole mess. Such a churning of water by sharks! (We counted four species of small and large ones happily eating huge chunks of salt beef.) Some one must have read about the buccaneers diet of "salt junk" and extended the idea to Cuban dietary. Residents in tropical lands do not like highly salted foods! But then war time always brings out strange characters with great authority who seem to be in hiding and silent during the short intervals of peace.

KEEPING FOODS SAFE FROM ENTEROTOXIN

In 1934, we worked out a practical method for keeping susceptible foods safe from staphylococcal toxin production. After numerous researches on the times and temperatures needed for toxin production in various foods, we found that toxin was not formed below 55° or above 120° F. At 61° F to 115° F, the inoculated cocci grew. Determining the growth curves in broth, ham mash, sliced ham, rice and bread pudding, milk, egg sauces, soups, gravies, poultry stuffings, etc., we found the lag period, logarithmic phase, and stationary phase to vary according to the temperature, time held, and character of the substrate food, i.e. if nonacid and containing more than 30-35 per cent moisture. The shortest period and time for toxin formation was 4.5 hours at 92° F; at 65° F, 10 hours, and at 115° F, 9 hours. There were more data, but to condense the story, we found that the *Incubation Danger Zone* should be defined for safety as 50° F to 120° F, and the time as 4 hours. We used to tell food handlers, "Keep it hot or keep it cold or eat it at once!" Many human-volunteer tests with slices of ham sprayed with known enterotoxin formers and held at 40° F and 43° F for two weeks, when pasteurized (culinary heating does not nullify staphylococcal toxin; it is heat stable) and eaten did not cause any distress. The yellow slime of the staphylococci was washed off for esthetic reasons. The data were very useful in trials of cases. These bacteria form enterotoxin during their logarithmic phase of growth. The lag phase usually lasts about 1.5 hours in a very nutrient medium and 2 hours in salted, cured meats. For full information of these phases of microbiology including flow sheet analyses of food processing, see our *Microbiology of Meats* and *Meats and Meat Foods.*[22,23]

The human guinea pigs in all of these volunteer tests conducted by various groups were usually young medical students, biologists and microbiologists. The tester conductor had the potions (not portions) coded (some innocuous!). The brave young men and women stepped up and took their material to be ingested. They remained near headquarters. Never wear suspenders; the onset is sudden. Like Abe Lincoln's young lawyer friend in Springfield, Illinois, the partakers were not certain of their potion. According to the story, the young lawyer had practiced at the wrong bar too often and the local bar association forced him to take the pledge. One night at the tavern where the politicos and lawyers met to discuss problems of the day, the pledged one, who was drinking root beer, held his glass behind him and asked Mr. Lincoln, "Abe, would you pour a little whiskey into me glass unbeknownst to meself?"

SOME TYPICAL OUTBREAKS OF STAPHYLOCOCCAL ENTEROTOXIN ORIGINS

Personal investigations of all types of bacterial and chemical outbreaks—numbering about 300 where 4 persons to 500 persons were known to be involved, and about 1,200 investigations of episodes (1 to 3 persons involved)—were made over the years in the United States, Canada, and France. Some of the large outbreaks occurred in institutions, corporations, hospitals, hotels, restaurants, lunch and soda counters, schools, colleges, and the armed services. Many of the outbreaks took place in private homes and also at wedding parties served by caterers.

---

[22] Jensen, L. B.: *Microbiology of Meats*, 3rd ed. Champaign, Garrard Press, 1954, pp. 92-94.

[23] Jensen, L. B.: *Meat and Meat Foods: From Processor to Consumer.* New York, Ronald Press, 1949.

One outbreak which we often described to our students and to the officers in training at the Army Medical Service School at Chicago frequently excited mirth and also a few frowns. A missionary Bible school in Indiana, enrolling about two hundred students, served a group of one hundred young men about 6:00 P.M. The foods consisted of cheddar cheese sandwiches, pickles, milk, coffee, some dessert, and not much else. The students had been in the field all day, and many retired early. Around 8:00 P.M., a few men became nauseated, with cramping, and between 8:30 and 9:30 P.M., most of them were in the throes of acute *Staphylococcus* food poisoning. Some of the deep sleepers jumped out of bed at about 10:00 P.M. and joined the others. Many were ill and weak the next day, but physicians at the local hospital deemed them out of danger. The peccant food remained unknown to them. The next evening, some eighty other of the school students came in from their field of endeavor and ate the same cheese, but other kinds of foods, with the same violent symptoms ensuing. The officials then incriminated the cheese and we isolated numerous sticky mucoid, cream-colored colonies of staphylococci. When our monkeys were force-fed in triplicate the broth filtrate of these bacteria, all three of them were severely stricken. (One monkey died!) We tested the toxin in quite small doses and found it very potent for monkeys. A wag in our laboratory group named this bizarre culture *Staphylococcus ecclesiasticus*. The source of these bacteria and toxin in the cheeses was found to be a "dead vat" of milk which, when inoculated with lactic starter, incubated without the inhibitory lactic acid formation. It had been reseeded and finally soured. In the meantime, the toxin formers had entered the logarithmic phase in the milk and producd a very potent toxin. Like the Apostle Paul, the faithful endure much. All power to them! (The institution sued the cheesemaker for damages, however.)

Another cruel blow at a church affair occurred in a famous old community just north of Boston. The ladies of St. M_____'s parish had purchased a large number of dressed chickens to boil and bone which they did one forenoon. Placing the slices

in a large "hydrator" and placing the *compact, warm mass* in
the church basement refrigerator, they wound up their work
for the day. Next morning, preparing for the church benefit
lunch, the slices were made ready for chicken-salad sandwiches.
A large number of members came for the meal which began
about 11 A.M. By 2:00 or 3:00 P.M., every ambulance in greater
Boston hauled these stricken people to hospitals. All were suffering from acute *Staphylococcus* enterointoxication. The good
ladies had applied the letter of instruction for safe refrigeration
but not the precise technology. The statement in the New
Testament, "A little leaven leaveneth the whole lump," is as
true in this instance as it was in St. Luke's time. The compact,
warm slices could not be cooled under the conditions of storage and the *S. aureus,* which we isolated, had grown merrily
in their logarithmic phase.

A chef for the dining room of both office help and execu-
tives of a steel company also boiled a large number of dressed
chickens in several large boiling vats, turning off the gas burners at 2:00 A.M. At 7:00 A.M., kitchen help began boning the
chickens and preparing chicken salad to be served from 11:00
A.M. to 1:00 P.M. The boiled meat and juices were never refrigerated. At 1:00 P.M., the trouble began with the big brass
and chain-reacted down through the office help. It was staphylococcal poisoning with a vengeance. The chef informed us that
chicken salad had been prepared in this manner for all twenty-
three years of his service there. Our only comment was the
aphorism so often expressed by E. O. Jordan of The University
of Chicago, "In bacteriology, your sins will find you out."

Perhaps we dwell on staphylococcal intoxications at too-
great length. Citing just a few more outbreaks and episodes,
we will have done with this entity.

In an outbreak involving fifty-seven adult people eating at
a restaurant from 11:00 A.M. to 3:00 P.M., we were at loss to
point up the peccant food. Questionnaires finally pointed out
the culprit vector. Those who drank coffee without cream
escaped the intoxication. The creamer device was an old-fash-
ioned glass tube with supply can running vertically along the

large coffee urn. (These devices are not seen today). Getting
samples of cream from this device next day and counting on
nutrient agar and blood agar plates used in the early 1930's,
we isolated numerous *S. aureus* from whose filtrates toxin was
demonstrated in monkeys.

Another episode in which we personally participated occurred in Michigan from eating pancakes and waffles from
incubated mix (batters are usually pH 6.8 and contain 60 to
70% moisture—good media for staphylococci.) These batters are
often kept in the kitchen overnight and longer, in the Incubation Danger Zone.

Turkey dressing of many formulae, moist, nutrient, and
stuffed into the birds, often does not even reach pasteurizing
temperatures when the turkeys are deemed "done for serving."
Many tests with thermocouple devices show the center of the
dressing never to be warmer than 112° F.! Dressings should be
cooked or baked in trays separately. Double roasting of stuffed
turkeys i.e. partially roasted one day and "fully" processed the
next day, has caused many home episodes and outbreaks when
the toxic staphylococci have been present. Also, Type D streptococci, *Salmonella,* and *B. cereus* have been isolated in our
investigations of double-baked turkeys in food-borne illness.

During Navy maneuvers off San Diego, California, in 1937,
the galley service prepared hams by baking and served the
sliced meat to the officers' mess for the evening meal with no
unwanted results. Large portions of the meat were not refrigerated and were served with eggs to the crew next morning
with predictable results. A senior officer, radioing Dr. R. W.
Stone, then Director of the Los Angeles County Health Laboratory, for advice adding "What would we do if the Jap fleet
appeared off the horizon?" received the pragmatic reply: "Shoot
the damned hams over to the Japs!"

Staphylococci of a toxic variety, growing on boiled potatoes which were peeled and subsequently incubated for several
days, caused an outbreak in a large family of sharecroppers.
This outbreak was aired in a Texas county courtroom some
thirty-five years ago when the mother sued for damages alleg-

ing a commercially prepared baloney to be the offender (45-cent purchase). The cases of the nine children and father were allowed to be drawn up and consolidated for one trial with the mother's case. All had eaten the potatoes, but the baloney, bread; margarine, or hog grease (?); coffee, and milk were eaten sporadically, according to the questionnaire obtained from the minors, which fell out of the trial over objections. (Bacteriologists who recall the history of culture media will remember that sliced potato was the "solid medium" in use before gelatin and agar.)

The mother testified as to her illness on direct examination, but with natural female reticence only said, "I was as sick as a dog, and throwed up with misery." Upon rigorous cross-examination about her misery (which was not clearly food poisoning) we repeatedly asked her: "Is that all Mrs. X.? You must not have had much happen to you. Tell the court and jury (all men, of course) just what happened to you." This was a mistake, we learned. Never push a woman witness too far! Reddening and turning to the Judge she inquired in a huff: "Jedge, must I tell these men-folks just what happened to me?" "Yes, Mrs. X., you must. This is your day in court. Tell all," replied the judge with a benign smile. Turning in the witness chair and facing the male jurors, she shouted: "If you all must know jest what happened to me—I were so sick I done sit on one bucket and had my head in the othah!" A two-bucket job! The jurors roared with laughter and the defendants proceeded warily after this favorable jury reaction.

This story leading to the phrase, "two-bucket job" served us well in warning food handlers about processing culinary preparations and serving. They could understand the dramatics (of a sort) which pictured the situation in their minds. A two-bucket job is something to reckon with by anyone either in privacy or in public gaze. (This is especially true when experts in food poisoning work suffer a bout of enterointoxication.)

We encountered so many outbreaks and episodes that to recite more would be prolix except to stress the characters of the foods involved. These foods always contained over 30 per cent moisture, were nonacid in reaction, and had been in the Incubation Danger Zone over 4.5 hours. These criteria hold for other types of bacterial food-borne illness but not all.

Enterotoxin of staphylococci is antigenic, but heterologous toxic antigens do occur. The toxin is thermostable. Culinary heating and even autoclaving fifteen pounds for fifteen minutes did not destroy the toxin in ham slices in a human-volunteer test. Singularly enough, the enterotoxin, when refined for analysis and reported by Dack, consists of sixteen amino acids, but 50 per cent of the molecule (mol wt 24,000) consists of lysine, aspartic acid, glutamic acid, and tyrosine. It is water soluble and a protein. As in the case of botulinum toxins which also are proteins (made up of amino acids), there is no structural clue to their great toxicities although the pharmacologic effects are, of course, well known. The modes of action of staphylococcal enterotoxins do not involve glycolysis, cholinesterase, or the acetylation mechanism. In botulinum intoxication, more is known about these facets.

Treatment of patients suffering from enterointoxication usually consists of intravenous administration of standard salt-glucose solution to offset mineral imbalance and dehydration, since chlorine is lost by persistent vomiting and sodium by the severe diarrhea. Supportives are also given. We have observed fatalities in three children (dehydration and imbalance) not treated at all, one of whom was under the care of a physician who prescribed and diagnosed by telephone. Also, in the elderly and in cardiac cases we have observed fatalities. Otherwise the mortality rate is quite low in this type of food-borne illness.

Antibiotic-induced enterocolitis—the physician's problem—is quite well known now after the introduction of the tetracycline antibiotics. Before this side effect was recognized, we were defendants' witness in four trials of cases, three suits based upon the theory of implied warranty and one on negligence of a food processor and retailer. We all recall that in this induced illness, the normal intestinal flora are suppressed. Both staphylococci and type D streptococci-resistant strains (which are selected by the drug action) implant themselves in the lower intestinal tract.

If toxigenic or pathogenic, these bacteria cause continuous persistent irritation with diarrhea and distress. Often fungi and yeast forms could actually be seen by proctologic examinations. This is a long story not directly concerned with food, but in some of these cases when overtreatment persisted, high mortality rates ensued. Withdrawal of the drug and supportive treatments of choice often resulted in slow recovery from this dangerous malady. Likewise, induced mutations, selection, or emergence of resistant phage groups of enterotoxic and virulent staphylococci became a grave hospital problem the world over.

SALMONELLAE

THE SALMONELLA were so named for Dr. D. E. Salmon, former Chief of the Bureau of Animal Industry, United States Department of Agriculture, who first described a member of this group in 1885. Over one thousand serotypes have now been distinguished. There has been a great deal of controversy on the role of *Salmonella* in food poisoning and food infection. Dack states: "Perhaps no field is more confused than the one concerned with the role of the *Salmonella* organisms in food poisoning." The confusion had centered on supposed toxin formation by the group and dosage of cells necessary to produce symptoms of illness in humans. Adequate methods for isolation and identification of these bacteria were wanting until quite recently. Much work remained to be done in quantitative determinations of these bacteria in various inocula, but good approximations can now be had.

Tests performed by Dack on twenty-four human volunteers, who were fed up to 11 ounces of cell-free filtrates and heat-killed broth cultures of nine strains of salmonella, failed to produce any symptoms of illness. Verder and Sutton[24] also tested filtrates and heated suspensions of *Salmonella* by feeding seven human volunteers, none of whom became ill. There can be no doubt that salmonella food poisoning is actually an infection and not an intoxication from supposed toxic substances of growth *in vitro*.

The dosage or numbers of salmonella necessary to elicit illness in humans has been studied by McCullough and Eisle,[25] who found that illness in prison volunteers resulted with S. *meleagridis* at 7.67 million cells and another strain required 24

---

[24]Verder, E. S., and Sutton, C.: *J. Infect. Dis.*, 53:262-271, 1933.

[25]McCullough, N. B., and Eisle, C. W. 1951. *J. Infect. Dis.*, 88:278-289; *J. Infect. Dis.*, 89:209-213 and 259-265; *J. Immunol.*, 66:595-608, 1951.

million cells. With *S. anatum,* the range was 587,000 and 860,000 levels for one strain and 44.5 million and 67.2 million levels for another. With *S. bareilly* and *S. newport,* the lowest dosage was 125,000 and 152,000, respectively. *S. derby* produced illness at the highest level fed—15,000,000 organisms, although five lower dosage levels were employed. *S. pullorum* was fed at eight dosage levels, but 1.3 to 10 billion organisms were required in order to produce illness.

The *Salmonella* are widespread in nature and have been found associated with man, mammals, birds, reptiles, and insects. Their presence in dust, soil, water, and unprotected foods is to be expected. Jordan[26] stated:

> . . . . Some investigators, especially German writers, regard them (*Salmonella*) as so widely distributed in Nature that any attempt to control the spread of infection is like fighting windmills. According to this view, the bacilli occur commonly in our every day surroundings and thence make their way rather frequently into a variety of foodstuffs.

Many standard examinations of air samples from streets, rooms of buildings, vacuum-sweeper dust, and swabbings of surfaces in areas inhabited by animals and man frequently show *Salmonella* of many serologic groups, as well as other enteric bacteria. Human carriers, rodents, Aves, and flies spread these bacteria. Wherever fecal coliform bacilli are found, *Salmonella* may be expected, and many examinations show this to be the case. We live in an environment where salmonella may be present in sparse or moderately low numbers.

Salmonella typhi infections, once a planetary scourge, have become a rarity in our country, thanks to immunizing inoculations and the disciplines of sanitation. Novelists in the period 1870-1908, who had characters in their stories whom they wished to exit in some unhappy fashion, transplanted them to Chicago where they died of typhoid fever caused by *"Bacillus typhosus."* During those times, the city's raw, untreated sewage, contain-

---

[26] Jordan, E. O.: *Food Poisoning and Food-Borne Infection,* Chicago, University of Chicago Press, pp. 154-155, 1931.

ing *Salmonella* and other enteric microorganisms and viruses, was discharged directly into Lake Michigan. Water from the intakes nearby was pumped back to the city supply untreated, thus recycling the pathogens many times. This resulted in very high morbidity and mortality rates of typhoid fever and intestinal diseases.

During the years 1900 to 1925, the classification of "intestinal gram-negative rods" or "gram-negative enterics" was in a sad state of unclarity. *B. coli* was known well enough, as was *B. aerogenes*, mainly from the needs of the water bacteriologist and sanitarian. The pathogens, both typhoid-paratyphoid and dysenteries (B. *Shiga-Kruse*), and *Alcaligenes, Proteus, Cloacae,* etc., were, in differential tables for classification, lumped together for fermentation and other simple reactions. We were familiar with the "Aertryke and Morseele bacilli" as well as scores of other designations of ill-defined taxonomy, usually names of discoverers and geographic areas. (As a soldier we recall the villages of Aertryke and Morseele in Belgium during World War I and readily acquiesced to such bacillary names (now *Salmonella*) from the sanitary aspects of these villages alone.)

When E. O. Jordan was asked for transplants of his extensive paratyphoid culture collection, the request came, "Dear Professor, will you please send me transplants of *Salmonella?*" The good professor answered that he did not have *Salmonella* but he would mail some paratyphoid cultures! This was in 1923. When the somatic and flagellar serologic methods for distinguishing serotypes gradually came to the fore after careful, controlled research (P. R. Edwards' name will always be closely associated with this progress), the taxonomic picture broadened into a thousand or more serotypes. This was all to the good, since the epidemiologist could now trace sources of *Salmonella* (the sources were legion) and the physician could distinguish the etiology of fevers and gastrointestinal varieties of illnesses due to these bacteria with preciseness if he engaged laboratory facilities.

The paracolon groups were also found to occur extensively in nature, and some serotypes possessed virulence of Salmonella (and eventually some of these strains were so named, like the S. *arizona* group, but was again reclassified as a paracolon). Bacteriologists and other sanitarians in convention at Colorado Springs some years ago suffered food poisoning from a member of the paracolon group.

Nature never respects persons. The national Convention of Bacteriologists held at the Edgewater Beach Hotel in Chicago two decades ago affords another striking example of the "hydrant wetting the dog." Baked Alaska—an egg-containing frozen ice-cream confection— was served at the banquet about 7:00 to 8:30 P.M. to six hundred in attendance. Early next morning, food-borne salmonellosis began to manifest itself with diarrhea and other aspects of this infection, including hasty movements and loss of dignity. Not all persons at risk were affected at that time, and several busloads of bacteriologists departed for Notre Dame University to inspect the Sterile Animal Laboratory. In all, 360 persons became ill. Bus drivers told us that all along the route from Chicago to South Bend, Indiana, there were "frequent, urgent cries for stops." Few reached South Bend. Enough of our "Chicago Clout" pressured the Daily Press to ignore the outbreak, but a year afterwards, the Saturday Evening Post carried a paragraph on its editorial page mentioning the melancholy event. Salmonella were isolated from the "baked Alaska" ingredients (S. *montevideo* in frozen egg whites).

The existing pertinent literature on Salmonella is so voluminous that to continue further, one experiences the futility of the pioneer farmer who set plough on his two whole sections of pristine Iowa prairie land. Gazing at the horizon, he called out to his mule hitched to the plough: "Go any damn way you want to, mule! We ain't going to finish this season."

THE ROLE OF STREPTOCOCCI (LANCEFIELD TYPE D) IN FOOD-BORNE GASTROENTERITIS AND ENTERITIS

WE INVESTIGATED thirty-eight outbreaks and episodes caused by *Streptococcus faecium* and *S. fecalis*. In our series, there were 898 persons made ill in these outbreaks and incidents. The literature on streptococcal food-borne disease lists eleven different species of this genus as causal agents, but we never encountered the other nine species or variants in our investigations of outbreaks and laboratory studies. There were twenty-six different foods involved.

It will be recalled that alpha streptococci produce a halo of green choleglobin (not methemoglobin) on blood agar media, but fall into two Lancefield serologic groups, D. and B. *S. faecalis* and *S. faecium*, both D types, were identified long ago by Orla-Jensen of Copenhagen. These two strains are very closely related, and controversy arose as to their identity as food poisoners. Thus, we selected strains of *S. faecium* (sorbitol negative, arabinose positive, etc.) and conducted human-volunteer feeding tests.

Four male volunteers (the writer was one of them) were fed one-half pint of milk soured with *S. faecium* (about 750 million per ml).

> Volunteer A became ill (diarrhea only with cramps) and remained afebrile. Onset was in 12 hours.
>
> Volunteer B had the same symptoms in 10 hours.
>
> Volunteer C had no symptoms.
>
> Volunteer D had the same symptoms as A and B. Onset was in 18 hours.

A ham was deliberately infected by arterial introduction of broth culture, incubated twenty-four hours at 37° C, and sampled, showing about 250 million per gram. Slices weighing 150 to 250 gm were then fed to these volunteers.

Volunteer A at first feeding (250 gm) had severe diarrhea, cramping, slight nausea, no vomiting. Onset was in 8 hours. Mr. A., after ten days "partook" of 200 gm of this ham (refrigerated) and again became ill with the same symptoms. Onset was in 10 hours.

Volunteer B ate 150 gm and had the same symptoms as A. Onset was in 10 hours.

Volunteer C also had the same symptoms as A. Onset was in 7 hours.

Volunteer D backed out this time because of "prior commitments."

Later, this strain of *S. faecium* in 24-hour glucose broth culture was fed in estimated numbers of one-half billion cells to three of the volunteers. Volunteers A, B, and C, if they had not been at risk, would not have noticed one or two loose stools. They had no symptoms. Volunteer D remained aloof. These broth-grown streptococci failed to produce frank illness under these conditions.

Sterile ham mash was inoculated and held at 37° C for twenty-six hours. The estimated numbers were *circa* 700 million per milliliter of mash. This preparation was fed in 150 ml amounts.

Volunteer A became ill with diarrhea and cramping, some nausea but no vomiting. Onset was in 10 hours.

Volunteer B had the same symptoms as A. Onset was in 10 hours.

Volunteer C had the same symptoms as A. Onset was in 7.5 hours.

Volunteer D did not show up.

The remaining ham mash was refrigerated, and one week later was heated to 170° F. for twenty minutes to insure sterility of this strain. Plate and serial dilution tests showed no viable streptococci (D types are quite resistant and survive at 149° F for fifty minutes in 48-hour broth cultures, at 160° F for ten minutes in wet turkey dressing but not at 165° F for six minutes).

All four men volunteered, and each swallowed 150 ml of the heated mash. They remained free of symptoms. Under these conditions, there were no toxic metabolites present.

There is a relatively large literature on streptococcal food poisoning (we collected sixty-five journal articles in the literature up to 1957), and the subject is by no means clarified in all aspects.

Mark Twain, when suddenly called upon to speak at an English University dinner many years ago, arose unsteadily to his feet and began: "Caesar was a great man, but he is dead. Hannibal was a great man, but he is also dead. . . . and I don't feel very well myself." He thereupon fled to the men's room, activated by some type of intestinal irritation. This appears to be the status of the subject at present. (Mark ate some British cold roast beef.)

Large numbers of these cells must be ingested to induce illness. The question of toxic metabolites is not settled, since Buchbinder *et al.* observed onsets in two to ten hours in their human-volunteer tests, suggesting preformed toxins. Furthermore, they observed that S. *faecalis* grown five hours produced illness in human volunteers but if 24-hour cultures were fed, no illness resulted.

Dack, observing, as we did, that these bacteria decarboxylate tyrosine to tyramine, fed human volunteers large doses of tyramine without producing illness. In other feeding tests, he observed illness in volunteers partaking of a strain which had caused spontaneous illness in a canned Vienna-sausage outbreak. At that time, Dack felt his studies indicated that a potent strain for volunteers must be grown in the same kind of food as the peccant food in outbreaks. Those patients being treated for hypertension with Eutron® must avoid tyramine-containing foods. Tyramine is often lethal with Eutron® medication—an adjuvant action with this pressor compound.

We fed thirty-eight adult rhesus monkeys 100 ml of 24-hour whole-brain broth cultures of S. *faecium* and S. *faecalis*. Only one monkey became slightly ill (diarrhea in ten hours), which may have been due to some other cause, since on occasion one monkey in a laboratory colony does develop diarrhea lasting for a day or so. In human-volunteer tests and in outbreaks both large and small, the persons suffering this type of illness recover rapidly.

In one outbreak which we investigated in Springfield, Ohio, involving some 800 persons at risk (perhaps 150 ill but 75 persons interviewed only) from turkey dressing, the women presented some gastrointestinal involvement, but the males suffered diarrhea and cramping (little nausea) only. Recovery was rapid. Onset ranged from seven to twenty hours (median eleven hours). *S. fecaelis* was isolated from the dressing salvaged from the caterer-hotel kitchen. The blood agar plate counts and serial dilution counts in glucose-brain broth tubes were high, ranging from 500,000 to two million per gram of dressing and giblets.

Several "ivory tower" bacteriologists who are known *not* to have had practical experience in this field scoffed at the fact that S. *fecalis* and S. *faecium* can cause food-borne illness! Their posture and stance, based upon a few feeding tests with old laboratory strains, transferred uncounted times, is still maintained by them. Perhap not all of the D-type species can induce food-borne illness, but the number of outbreaks, incidents, and volunteer tests definitely place S. *fecalis* and S. *faecium* in the food-poisoning category.

BOTULISM

Botulism derived this clinical name from sausage. (Latin, *botulus*), a supposed source or "vector" of the disease. Physicians of southern Germany in 1800 noted that lethal intoxications were caused by eating certain large spoiled sausages. *Botuli* of many formulae had been made in classical times.[27] Roman market police, who controlled sale of meat foods, exacted fines and directed that *botuli* and other foods which they had condemned should be thrown into the Tiber river.[28]

In 1896, Van Ermengen (*Rev. d'Hygiene, 18*:1-61) proved that botulism was a poisoning due to a specific spore-forming anaerobic bacillus which secreted a powerful neurotoxin. During the past sixty-five years, the poisoning has been traced to numerous foods, both vegetal and animal in origin—especially glass-packed nonacid foods processed at home by the dangerous cold-pack method. This method of "food preservation," which did not kill spores of anaerobes, had long been in use by housewives and strangely enough was recommended to housewives by the Food Control Committee of our country during World War I, whose slogan was "Food will win the War." Naturally, humble bacteriologists protested the method, but "political scientists" of Washington, D. C., of those days (not trained in science excepting perhaps, political astrology) thought otherwise, and this ill-conceived processing was not stamped out until World War II times when home and mobile pressure sterilizers came into vogue.

Commercially canned foods of American origin such as ripe olives, tuna, and many other nonacid foods have caused only three outbreaks in this country since 1927 when schedules for

---

[27] M. Gabius Apicius: Translated by J. D. Vehling. Chicago, Walter M. Hill, 1936.

[28] Jensen, L. B.: *Man's Foods.* Champaign, Garrard Press, 1953, pp. 137-141.

adequate times and temperatures for processing were, by long and arduous tests, published by the National Canners Association, the University of California (Hooper Foundation of San Francisco under the directorship of Dr. K. F. Meyer), and the University of Chicago (Ricketts Laboratory under the chairmanship of E. O. Jordan).

Grants-in-aid were given by the National Canners Association to university laboratories. The writer, in 1923, received his stipend of $33.00 per month, together with $66.00 per month from the University of Chicago for other duties. This was all to the good, frayed sleeves notwithstanding. (A recent story also points up this sleeve condition: Young Franklin, eager to impress his father about learning things at school, cried in youthful haste and transposition, "Dad, it was President Lincoln who frayed the sleeves." Grim Republican father corrected his offspring with, "No, my son, Lincoln freed the slaves; it was a couple of later presidents who frayed the sleeves!"

The journal literature on botulism is now too vast in scope to attempt listings.[29-32] Here again, we shall limit our survey of the subject to personal observations. There are five antigenically different toxins formed by *C. botulinum* (Types A, B, C, D, E), i.e. the specific antitoxins are able only to neutralize their homologous toxins. After a complete study of this specificity, we published a paper[33] in 1926, showing that very large doses of Type A or of Type C antitoxin exerted some slight neutralizing power upon Type B toxin. Since the toxins have greater avidity for nerve tissues than for antitoxins, this method of therapy is of

---

[29]Dack, G. M.: *Food Poisoning,* 2nd ed. Chicago, University of Chicago Press, 1956, chap. 4.

[30]Meyer, K. F.: *Food Poisoning. New Eng. J. Med.* 249:765, 804, 843, 1953.

[31]Tanner, Fred and Tanner, Louise: *Food Poisoning and Food-Borne Infections.* 2nd ed. Champaign, Garrard Press, 1954.

[32]Jensen, L. B.: *Microbiology of Meats.* 3rd ed. Champaign, Garrard Press, 1953.

[33]Jensen, L. B.: *Some influences of antitoxic and other serums on botulinum intoxications. J. Infect. Dis.,* 39:413-423, 1926.

doubtful value unless polyvalent serum is administered shortly after ingestion of a peccant food. Usually the poisoning is not detected until symptoms are evident.

The spores of *C. botulinum* are found worldwide in soils, but in the past when farmers used domestic animals' manures for crop soils, such soils, upon testing, did not harbor these spores as frequently as pristine soil, i.e. virgin soils, and chemically fertilized soils. Spores from the soil and dust are very heat-resistant. The Hooper Foundation's tests with spores in large inocula prepared from laboratory cultures showed that A and B spores require the following:

> 2.78 minutes at 250° F for kill
> 10.00 minutes at 240° F for kill
> 36.00 minutes at 230° F for kill
> 150.00 minutes at 220° F for kill
> 330.00 minutes at 212° F for kill

Presumably, the problem of explaining greater heat resistance of spores found in soil compared with lesser resistances of spores from laboratory strains has not been resolved. Actually, some laboratory-produced A and B spores have such low resistance to heat that tests in standard thermal death-time cans are equivocal, even with very large inocula. Many experiments have been performed for the purpose of increasing resistance of botulinum spores to heat and for canning tests with new foods and different sizes of containers. Professor Fred Tanner and others devoted much time to this work without success. The writer employed composite soil samples from many North American sites as inocula for critical tests (samples showing type A spores in circa 1/10 grams of soil[34]). Animal intestinal

---

[34]Incubated at 70° C and 92° F to prevent growth of thermophiles. This technique is involved and used only occasionally for critical tests with resistant spores. *C. sporogenes* are also isolated in the soil samples, but A and B spores are not affected as the A and B toxins (which become nullified or destroyed by *C. sporogenes*). A source of thermophilic spores is soybean meal and flour— sometimes harboring 500,000 to 5 million spores per gram. We employed these inocula in lieu of laboratory spores in canning tests which then suggested known virgin-soil samples for resistant spores of *C. botulinum* A or B. Virgin soils from the Rocky Mountain valleys and British Columbia were often suitable for these limited tests.

passage did not increase resistance of laboratory spores, as in the case of experiments performed with *C. perfringens* spores by Betty Hobbs of England.

The problem of escalated resistance of spores to heat in oil-fat menstrua was investigated by us long ago. The broad details of these investigations, together with the literature on the subjects can be found in our *Microbiology of Meats*, 3rd ed. (Champaign, Garrard, 1954, pages 272-278). For instance, botulinum spores in tuna in cottonseed oil were killed in 320 minutes at 212° F, but in phosphate buffer required only 210 minutes at 212° F. Again in the oil, these spores required 36 minutes at 230° F for kill but only nine minutes at 212° F for kill in the phosphate solution. The entrapment of spores in oil-in-water or water-in-oil emulsions always presents a hazard when they eventually germinate and form toxin. The vagaries of spore crops are many and subtle. We pointed out some of these variations to be kept in mind by the practical bacteriologist (see "spores" in index of book cited above).

Washed spores can be swallowed with impunity, as revealed by many animal tests. The spores germinate into bacilli under anaerobic conditions and when incubated at 55° F to 110° F in nonacid hydrated mediums. The toxins are the most poisonous substances known to science and will penetrate any mucous membrane—lips, conjunctiva, nose, mouth, throat, and the entire intestinal tract. These toxins, like the dinoflagellate poisons from "Red Tide" (affecting shell fish and fish in certain marine waters), hinder synthesis or the release of acetylcholine from the nerve endings. Ascending paralysis begins with characteristic symptoms in 12 to 108 hours (usually 24 to 36 hours). There is little or no gastrointestinal irritation. Constipation is the rule, with double vision, fatigue, headache, difficulty in swallowing (drooling), and heavy breathing, but the mind remains alert. Death results from respiratory failure. The fatality rate runs from 60 to 95 per cent in the few outbreaks we have personally investigated, although the textbooks state the mortality rate as about 65 per cent. Most of these outbreaks were caused by Types A and B toxins. Only one case of Type C has been recorded (in France) and no Type D outbreaks, except in horses are on record. All of these toxins are destroyed by boiling and even lower temperatures will nullify them.

Type A	toxin	6	minutes	at	176° F
		18	minutes	at	162° F
		85	minutes	at	149° F
Type B	toxin	15	minutes	at	176° F
Type C	toxin	30	minutes	at	176° F
Type E	toxin	1	minute	at	144° F

Type E, the "marine toxin," has caused death and grave illness in British Columbia, Japan, the Pacific states, Iceland, and especially in the USSR around the Black Sea.

Smoked lake (freshwater) fish vended in oxygen-impermeable wrappers have harbored type E toxins on occasion and, *C. botulinum* type E may either be introduced in (1) solar sea salt desirable for curing fish, (2) oceangoing craft carrying them into inland waters through new freshwater shipping lanes, (3) water fowl carriers, (4) contamination from marine products, and (5) contamination from spores native to these regions. The facts are not known as this is written.

At the close of World War II, Iceland herring packed in tierces and salted (one consignment to Denmark and Norway) harbored Type E organisms and toxin, causing outbreaks. (The outbreaks were not published but known to their state fisheries laboratories.) Also, a batch of frozen whale meat in Canada was found to harbor botulinum toxin (type not divulged) in 1949. Canned tuna also transgressed in the United States a few years ago with Type E toxin.

The stock spore is not very heat resistant in our series (five to thirty minutes at 212° F, but some strains required 180° F for thirty minutes), and Type E toxin was destroyed in the incubator overnight at 98° F! The prepared seafoods—salmon, tuna, herring, sturgeon, when infected are very poisonous as are the other types of botulinum toxins. These type E clostridia grow at low temperature (43°, but also at 38° F!)

Most of the toxic foods in which *C. botulinum* have grown herald the presence of toxin by "off odors"—rancid butter-like odors, putrid odors especially in protein foods and less marked in vegetal and non-acid home canned foods. Type E does not give much organoleptic warning! This is true when grown in canned tuna.

We were the first to determine that critical brine concentrations, i.e. ratio of salt to moisture can inhibit type A and B botulinum spore germination and growth with toxin production. For instance, consider the following problem.

57 % moisture in meats
3.5% salt (NaCl)
———
divide 60.5   into 3.500 salt equals (times 100) 5.78% brine.

This brine prevents toxin formation and spore germination in heat-processed canned meats. The spores and cells will not grow when the meat or rehydrated foods contain less than 30-33 per cent moisture. Also, foods acid in reaction (pH 5.0 to 4.3) do not provide suitable substrates, provided other microorganisms do not neutralize the acidity as in home-canned (glass-packed) tomatoes.

The first case of botulism seen personally by us occurred in northwestern Iowa some fifty years ago. We accompanied Dr. J. W. Morrison, a talented general practitioner, who recognized the classic symptoms of "botulinus" intoxication in an elderly male patient whose family had belatedly called him from their rural home. All of the textbook symptoms were seen, and treatment, except with palliatives, was obviously of no avail. Serums were not available at this time and would have proved of little or no benefit. Home cold-pack chicken meat was most probably the peccant food. This paralyzed patient died from respiratory failure as expected. Chickens which had been fed throw-away contents of the glass-jar lot developed "limber neck" which proved the nature of the fatality. Typing was not done.

Another outbreak in North Dakota occurred from a rural get-together dinner. Home, cold-pack vegetal and animal-derived foods were served. The peccant food or foods were in doubt. Most of the guests who drank deeply of illicitly distilled liquor (the prohibition lid was on from the Volstead Act) escaped death from botulism, but the "teetotalers" died—one after several days of delayed symptoms.

The effect of grain alcohol or ethanol on botulinum toxins had been reported in sober, dignified journals and books. For instance, Armstrong, Story, and Scott (Public Health Reports *34*, 2877-2905) in 1919 found that botulinum toxins could be nullified by 32% ethyl alcohol (final concentration). This result was obtained by injecting guinea-pigs intraperitoneally or subcutaneously with 20 MLD doses of toxin. It had been observed that two people partaking of alcohol did not die in an outbreak. Bronfenbrenner and Schlesinger (*Proc. Soc. Exp. Biol. 18*:304-305; *J. Exp. Med.*, 38, 509, 1924) also observed that 20% to 30% ethanol in the toxic mixture nullified the toxin in ten minutes. Topley and Wilson (*Principles of Bacteriology and Immunity*, Baltimore, Williams & Wilkins, 1938, p. 1276) stated, "alcohol precipitates botulinum toxin, and it is possible that frequent small doses of brandy might prove beneficial." Tanner and Tanner (*Food-Borne Infections and Intoxications*, Champaign, Garrard Press, 1953, p. 555) describe survival of people eating toxin-containing foods and partaking of alcoholic drinks and suggest nullification of toxin in German dietaries where alcoholic drinks are used more at meals—"perhaps more than in America."

Another episode involving "alcohol therapy" may be worth recording. A brilliant food bacteriologist of an industrial research laboratory was titrating type A botulinum toxin of great potency. Failing to use rubber-bulb suction pipettes, he accidentally sucked up some diluted toxin into his mouth. The cotton plug in the pipette was too densely packed. Knowing the avidity of toxin for red membranes he washed out his mouth and throat thoroughly with soapy water. The director of the laboratory then prepared a sugar solution of diluted reagent ethanol (grain alcohol) and persuaded the bacteriologist to quaff the "antidote," which medicine was taken without protest. In the meantime, polyvalent antitoxin (the only serum available) was ordered and on its way to the patient's home. The patient obviously was exhilarated during the auto ride to his house and upon reaching his front porch danced a fast-beat jig. The escorts rapped timidly on the door. The wife answered and perceiving immediately the state of her husband, demanded an explanation. She was told the *true* story. Her reaction was summed up by exclaiming: "Well! I've heard many excuses but this is the darndest excuse I have ever heard!" The bacteriologist recovered uneventfully with nothing graver than a "binge headache." Happily, there was no side effect from the administration of serum.

During those times when prohibition was supposedly in effect, some scientists at stag dinners always viewed certain foods with distrust and dutifully took liberal swallows of "antidote" with hearty skoals and terminal mutterings of "bots!" However, we do not recommend alcoholic antidotes as a safeguard against botulinum intoxication. Let St. Paul's advice be the guide: "Take a little wine for thy stomach's sake."

Botulinum toxins are generally conceded to be the most poisonous substances yet discovered. The lethal dose for white mice may be as little as 950 molecules—less than 10^{-13} gm/kg. These anticholinesterase toxins lower the concentration of acetylcholine to paralytic levels by preventing synthesis or release of acetylcholine from nerve endings.

The unprecedented toxicity of botulinum toxins, notably certain strains of Type A, led some foreign military strategists to inquire by means of their agents how such unprecedented toxicities were produced under laboratory methods of culture (1925). No one in authority at that time was interested in this situation.

A-type toxin was eventually crystallized and showed toxicities of 32 billion intraperitoneal LD_{50} per gram of dry toxin in white mice (molecular weight of 10^6). The toxin is composed of nineteen amino acids. The extreme toxicities of crystalline A toxin and purified type B toxin cannot be accounted for from the analytical data or tentative structural formulae.

GENUS BACILLUS

B. CEREUS, A SPORE-FORMING aerobic rod, has been the etiologic agent in several outbreaks in Europe and the United States. Fatalities are not recorded. We saw only two cases, one case in a child who drank "sweet curdled" milk deemed edible or "potable." The genus *Bacillus* is usually the cause of "sweet curdling" and a sample of "incipient spoiled" milk in this category may contain very high counts of this species and other members of the genus *Bacillus*. *B. cereus* is related in biochemical and serological reactions to *B. anthracis*. A *B. subtilis* extract (protease) is now used in laundry detergents.

CLOSTRIDIUM PERFRINGENS

There are three different species in different genera of bacteria which cause almost identical symptoms in outbreaks of food-borne infections. These species are *C. perfringens*, *B. cereus*, *S. fecalis* and *S. faecium*. In both human-volunteer tests and in outbreaks, the onset of symptoms may range from four to twenty hours with a median of ten to twelve hours. Statistical analysis of this incubation period in humans does not serve the epidemiologist precisely because the symptomology includes nausea, cramps, colic, and diarrhea. Vomiting is not a constant feature but is seen in a few males and more often in women and children.

The times and temperatures for destruction of spores of *C. perfringens* are ordinarily the following:

Phosphate buffer-broth

185° F	80 minutes
194° F	35 minutes
203° F	15 minutes
212° F	10 minutes

Dry spores on glass slides

248° F	50 minutes

266° F   20 minutes
284° F   12 minutes
338° F   7 minutes
500° F   2 minutes
752° F   20 seconds

The British bacteriologist, Betty Hobbs, who has done most of the work in this area found that after intestinal passage, some spores of strains of *C. perfringens* resisted 212° F for five hours but were killed in six hours at boiling temperatures. Recultivation lessens this resistance. Our problems are never simple!

The few outbreaks owing to *C. perfringens* which we investigated are well illustrated by one typical large outbreak following a pre-Thanksgiving dinner in a factory dining room. The peccant food was found to be wet turkey dressing "roasted in the birds" and "held at room temperatures" for two days prior to serving. There were about 200 persons at risk. Of these adults, both men and women, 142 were made ill with symptoms as given above, and onset ranged from six hours to twenty-two hours with a median time of twelve hours. All recovered in twelve hours to four days without sequelae.

Another scattered outbreak occurred in 1930 from a butter substitute—the starter being a strain of *C. perfringens* which produced very little gas in lactose. During the early 1920's Dr. Stewart Koser found starters for salt-rising bread which were pure cultures of *C. perfringens* (or *C. welchii* as the species was then called). Up to 1958, the Food and Drugs Administration reported on 40 outbreaks from this organism—the majority caused by turkey meats (and dressing) held out of refrigeration overnight. British reports recorded 308 cases of *C. perfringens* food poisoning in the two-year-period of 1955 to 1957. A large outbreak in Sweden was described in 1952. There were 1,034 persons at risk, and 583 became ill. The peccant food was fish ("pike-perch") incubated before serving. Textbooks describe many more outbreaks but no fatalities.

FOOD-BORNE VIRAL DISEASES,
INCLUDING HEPATITIS

IN SOME OUTBREAKS of illnesses owing to foods and drink, the conventional etiologic factors are not discovered by laboratory examinations of "comestibles and patients." The literature on these cases has grown during the past decades. Since these types of infections are thought to be viral in origin (and so proven in some cases like the F. S. strain and Marcy strain of intestinal viruses), it is important that a differential diagnosis be attempted. These infections simulate the symptoms of food poisoning, although epidemic diarrhea and vomiting are more readily differentiated. Our knowledge of nonbacterial gastroenteritis leaves much to be desired. This is well illustrated by the diagnosis of "intestinal flu."

Human volunteers swallowing fecal filtrates have shown the F. S. viral and Marcy viral strains to be real offenders as causes of gastroenteritis, but human volunteers in these experiments cause attending physicians great apprehension. There are a lot of "failures" in reproducing these supposedly viral illnesses, but earnest investigators can take heart from Hooton's early experience in conducting verbal and physical tests with *Homo sapiens*. When he was a young Harvard graduate student in physical anthropology, Hooton observed a stately black-haired blue-eyed lady walking down Court Street in Boston, leading by the hand her small red-haired, brown-eyed son. Stepping up and doffing his hat to the lady, Dr. Hooton said, "Madam, I am a student of hair and eye-color inheritance. Your son and you present a striking difference in coloration. May I inquire about the hair color of the father of the boy?" Whereupon the stately lady, eyeing the inquisitive student accoster, replied with sadness in her voice, "Sonny, I'll be damned if I know. He didn't take his hat off!"

The virus of infectious hepatitis is differentiated from the virus of serum hepatitis by differences in (1) incubation period, (2) routes of natural dissemination, and (3) specific immunity conferred by each virus. Both viruses can be transmitted to man by needles. About 20 to 120 days are required for the agent of infectious hepatitis to produce the disease, while approximately 60 to 160 days represent the corresponding period for serum hepatitis. The presence of serum hemagglutinin for chicken erythrocytes may prove to be a diagnostic aid in differentiating hepatitis from jaundice due to other causes.

This virus is very heat resistant and one of the most thermostable of the known viruses. It withstands boiling in water for three hours and in serum is killed in twenty minutes at 250° F. In dried serum preparations subjected to dry heat, the virus is "killed" in sixty minutes at 320° F.

When the jaundice is medically induced by needles and transfusions, the mortality rates are higher than in cases of ingestion routes. In the first fourteen weeks of 1959, there were 7,601 cases reported in the United States. The incidence of viral hepatitis is high the world over, and preventive measures are wanting (as this is written, although tissue cultures may soon be a reality). A classical outbreak was reported by Roos of Gothenburg in 1956. Three physicians ate oysters together on November 26, 1955. One of these men at risk became ill with hepatitis on December 25, 1955. The other two became ill on December 27, 1955. Epidemiologists then found an engineer ill with hepatitis (December 21) who had eaten oysters at a restaurant on November 30, 1955. Five persons out of nine at risk who had eaten Gothenburg-produced oysters on November 28 became ill. Four guests at this home served dinner did not eat oysters and remained well. Finally, 119 cases of viral hepatitis were traced to a wholesaler whose osyters were stored in wells in a boat harbor where the municipal drainage system emptied.

There have been other outbreaks resulting from the "sewage cycle" and individual cases where epidemiologists were not vouchsafed any clear-cut data. The Near East also appears to be well-seeded with the virus, especially those strains which have "avidity for Americans."

We had not worked in the field of poliomyelitis since 1929, except to isolate polio viruses from raw sewage and sludges in metropolitan sewage-treatment works. This was done by filtering the raw sewage and sludges, inoculating rhesus monkeys intracranially, and eventually, by feeding experiments. Routes of entry and peccant comestibles, as well as epidemiology and character of viral strains and vaccines are subjects too voluminous to be dealt with here. Most of the local outbreaks have yielded evidence on epidemiologic grounds only, but the ingestion route is obviously of the greatest importance.

The thermal destruction of polio viruses (Lansing strain, human fecal strains, rodent passage strains, monkey passage strains) have been determined with some preciseness, but in biology there appears to be but "one constant and that is variation." According to data of various workers, the heat and time for nullification of polio viruses in several substrates are:

water	131°	F	30	minutes
milk	143°	F	30	minutes
milk	163°	F	15	seconds
ice cream	175°	F	25	seconds
saline solution	140°	F	30	minutes
cream	163°	F	3	minutes

Water-borne "fevers," epidemic in extent, have been observed in Illinois (Rockford, 1912, and after the Chicago Union Stockyards fire, 1934). Clinically, these were virus infections in most cases, so far as clinicians were able to diagnose some of the individual cases. During the Chicago outbreak, we took a very active part in the epidemiology, analyses of potable and nonpotable waters, and recommendations for prevention of such outbreaks due to dual water supplies with crossconnections. A few cases of salmonellosis and amebic dysentery also occurred in this outbreak.

VOMITING AND DIARRHEA NOT CAUSED BY FOOD-POISONING BACTERIA

F<small>OOD POISONING</small> is often confused with other entities having no bearing whatsoever upon food-poisoning bacteria, gastrointestinal irritants, or enterotoxins. Vomiting or diarrhea, or both, are often associated with a great many diseases. Epidemic nausea and vomiting are described by Gray[35] and Dack.[36] The reader may consult the standard textbooks of medicine for detailed information. Vomiting and diarrhea are symptoms, not diseases. Wilbur and Washburn,[37] in a study of 140 cases of functional vomiting, found that continued vomiting occurring within an hour after meals is observed more often in women between the ages of twenty to forty years, of relatively healthy appearance, but presenting evidence of instability of the nervous system.

Dr. Wilbur E. Post of Chicago, in a personal communication, outlined some of the causes of gastrointestinal disturbances observed by him in his long practice and as a teacher of medicine. Other causes were learned at the Mayo Clinic:

1. Heart diseases such as angina ("indigestion"), thrombosis (coronary), decompensation with dyspnea or smothering, fibrillations, decompensation with abdominal distress.
2. Bright's disease, vascular type with hypertension. Manifestations of circulatory inefficiency may include fullness following meals and irritability of bowels with diarrhea.

---

[35]Gray, J. D.: *Brit. J. Med. J. 1,* 209, 1939.

[36]Dack, G. M.: *Amer. J. Digest. Dis., 8,* 210-211, 1941.

[37]Wilbur, Dwight L., and Washburn, R. N.: Clinical features of functional or nervous vomiting. *J. Amer. Med. Assoc. 110,* 477-480, 1938.

3. Gall bladder disease, causing irritability of colon with diarrhea and pain.

4. Diverticulitis with irritability of colon with diarrhea from eating bran, raspberry seeds, and apples with skins.

5. Chilling with diarrhea from vasomotor effect on vascular supply of intestines.

6. Cold foods and drinks and polluted water in which no etiologic agents can be detected.

7. Tobacco in excess in some few patients. Wines and liquors, especially claret.

8. Combinations of foods such as salads with sour dressing and milk, cherries and plums with milk, chocolate and beer.

9. Cold food or heavy meals when very tired.

10. Neurogenic and psychogenic disturbances with diarrhea, such as emotional disturbances, worries, hurry, quarrels, fear, functional vomiting.

11. Allergies and intermittent allergy.

12. "Intestinal flu" and virus—F. S. and Marcy Strains.

13. Encephalitis, etc., especially the St. Louis type.

14. Algid-comatose malaria, blackwater fever, yellow fever, etc.

15. High incidence of functional gastrointestinal disorders of pulmonary emphysema.

16. Uremia.

17. Pulmonary hypertension with syncope.

Of these categories, only sporadic cases occurred, i.e. one person only in a family with the obvious exceptions of viral infections.

Cases that came to trials in which we testified included an elderly man suffering from uremia (unknown to him); two cardiac cases poorly diagnosed; one gall bladder case in a woman who sued for damages for illness alleged to have been caused by eating pickled pigs' feet; one case where a forty-year-old woman, when investigated, was found to have consumed a dozen martinis daily for several weeks but alleged food poisoning from eating breakfast pork sausage; one case where a lady guitar player in New York city who alleged food poisoning from a designated food and, when investigated, was found to have nine personal-injury claims going at the same time (cases dismissed!). One lady in New Haven alleged illness from eating a pork product, but when investigated, was found to have a hospital record of pork allergy (case dismissed!) There were many more complaints investigated and fought by food processors during the Depression years, but with better financial times these complaints fell to low numbers. Thorough epidemiologic medical investigations as well as searches of the background of claimants and plaintiffs in affairs of this sort are obviously needed to clarify the individual pictures. The standard questionnaires which elicit important facts are of the greatest aid in evaluating the validity of food claims, both poisoning and foreign-substance injury. These investigational methods for determining the etiologic agents in outbreaks have been outlined precisely by the Federal Public Health Service, Training Branch, Communicable Disease Center of Atlanta, Georgia, and need not be elaborated upon here. Before this needed work was completed, we, over the years, determined the following:

1. Number of persons at risk
2. Number of persons ill
3. Symptoms
4. Times for onset of symptoms (median and scattered)
5. The peccant food or foods deduced from interrogation
6. History of the food implicated.

In many outbreaks and episodes, we failed to uncover any food or drink consumed as the carrier of etiologic agents, and also in cases and outbreaks like brucellosis, salmonellosis, shigellosis, viral hepatitis, and "intestinal flu" we failed to pinpoint the offending food, if any, or vehicle of infection—our alibili being that the longer incubation period had darkened memories of foods consumed or "the evidence had been eaten in the distant past." Comparing notes with others in this work, we found that we were not alone in these awkward situations, and above all, "misery loves company!" Naturally, the incubation period and precise modes of infection in brucellosis, viral hepatitis, and shigellosis are difficult to assess, and the vectors of infection often are beyond discovery. *Shigella* species infective for man are not carried by animals, as are *Salmonella*. *Brucella* are purported to have numerous portals of entry, and chronic brucellosis (a dreary disease) is difficult to diagnose precisely. Over 125 symptoms have been allegedly seen in all manifestations of brucellosis in humans! Certain strains of *Escherichia coli* (serologic $011B_4$, $055B_5$) have been associated with infantile diarrhea, and also in enormous inocula caused diarrhea in adult human volunteers.

UNCERTAIN ETIOLOGIES

IT WILL BE RECALLED that microorganisms require certain ranges of temperatures for growth. Classification in this respect is as follows:

Thermophiles range 110° F to 180° F
Mesophiles range 50° F to 109° F
Psychrophiles range 45° F to 15° F and lower

However, with exceptions, numerous genera and species are *facultative*, i.e. grow slowly or with flattened growth curves on media containing proper nutrilites and over 45% moisture. Examples are the *Achromobacter, Pseudomona, Flavobacterium, Clostridia* and the micrococci of several genera. Species of *Pseudomona* and *Achromobacter* are classroom examples, growing in ranges from 115° F to 15° F. Over the past forty years, claims have been made that species of psychrophiles (facultative) may cause food-borne infections, and that huge numbers of these cells, upon ingestion, can cause intestinal irritation. Human-volunteer feeding tests conducted by us have not borne out this assumption, but the theory is not dead. The late Dr. Samuel Prescott, Dean of the Massachusetts Institute of Technology observed some forty years ago that *Salmonella* grew slowly at 38° to 42° F on suitable foods held for one to several weeks, and the dosage of cells resulting could cause serious illness when ingested.

We have by no means exhausted this subject of food-borne illness of uncertain or unknown etiologies, and a patient perusal of the literature from 1880 to the present on claims for many different organisms as agents of gastrointestinal irritation will disclose facts and foibles in this area. Perhaps current lists of known food poisoners can be extended by suitable criteria. As an example of the complexities of criteria with "overtones" of temperature: Twelve puppies were fed grade A whole milk inoculated with *Achromobacter, Flavobacterium,* fluorescent pseudomonads, nonpathogenic micrococci, *B. subtilis* and Chinn's *Actinomyces.* The milk (not coagulated) showed high plate "counts" (*Circa* 30 million per milliliter). The animals lapped up the milk to satiety, for they were hungry in the morning. Six puppies were then placed in the 98° F. walk-in incubator room and the six remaining were allowed to play in their room held at 65° to 70° F. In eight hours, all of the pups in the large 98° F room were ill with diarrhea, whereas the puppies in the 70° F room did not become visibly ill at anytime. These dogs were under the care of Dr. Lawrence Frederic, a research veterinarian. The experiment was repeated by other groups and, at the time, was thought to shed some light on causes of summer diarrhea of infants.

LUMINOUS FOODS AND
PHOSPHORESCENT BACTERIA

T HE DAILY PRESS often carries stories of "glowing hams" and "lighted meats" and luminous foods of many kinds, since these occurrences provide good copy. Foods that "shine in the dark" from microbial contamination are not poisonous for man and animals. These bacteria are usually of marine origins, usually seafoods which contaminate home refrigerators and dealers' equipment. The luminous bacteria are facultative psychrophiles and facultative halophiles belonging to the genera *Photobacterium* and *Vibrio*, according to Breed's classification. There are two notices of fresh water luminescent bacteria—*Vibrio phosphorescens* and *Microspira phosphoreum*.[38]

The phenomenon was recorded by Aristotle, Bartholin, Robert Boyle, and Nicholas Lemery in 1720. In 1676, a Dr. Beale of England recorded in the Transactions of The Royal Society that a neck of veal suddenly became luminous "and shined so brightly that it did put the women into great affrightment."[39]

Public health people are often called on to allay fears of "radium contamination" in "lighted foods," and to explain the cause of the phenomenon, especially the nonpoisonous, noninfective nature of the phosphorescent bacteria (glowing in the dark like the firefly and glowworm). Sometimes a disgruntled householder would remind us of the old gag about "the beautifully glowing dead fish on the romantic seashore upwind at night, that stinks downwind like Beelzebub's spoor!"

We investigated four such outbreaks; one each in Spring-

---

[38]Jensen, L. B.: *Microbiology of Meats,* 3rd ed. Champaign, Garrard Press, 1954, pp. 298-300.

[39]Jensen, L. B.: *Meat and Meat Foods.* New York, Ronald Press, 1949, pp. 51-54.

field, Massachusetts; Mexia, Texas, Ft. Worth, Texas; and Chicago, Illinois. In all of these outbreaks, the fear of radium (and the unknown) motivated complaints about both cured and fresh meats glowing in the dark. During the Mexia, Texas, outbreak, the *New Yorker* suggested that dealers should dispense with neon lights and utilize luminous cuts of meat. In another case, an aged man on a strict diet stole downstairs at night and cut a piece of ham which "shined so brilliantly" that he fell over in fright and broke his hip. (He sued unsuccessfully for damages!)

Luminous bacteria are, in our experience, quite easily isolated. Culture a strip of shrimp or ocean fish and partly submerge the tissue in 3% salt solution at 20° C. After two or three days, streak on 3% salt nutrient agar containing 1.0% glycerol and 0.5% $CaCO_3$. Incubate plates at 40° F and 60° F and observe luminescent colonies in the dark room. We heard of sequelae only once in these cases: a luminescent *taillight* in a man which disappeared after a soapy bath. This affrightment was the worst that befell this complainant, but the "lights" were not personally visible to *him*, he said.

TRICHINOSIS AND FOOD TABOOS OF SEMITIC AND NEAR EASTERN NATIONS

Many Hebrew theologians as well as Christian and Muslim fellow-workers in this area of dietary laws and customs often discount hygienic and nutritional motives in the ancient taboos of Palestine and the Near East. Perhaps a midground should be attempted, encompassing both religious and utilitarian aspects of food acceptance. Taboos have been rife far through time and space with "all seventy nations of the earth" as the Septuagint visualized mankind. For the past half-century, cultural anthropologists and nutritionists have produced a useful literature on all phases of food acceptance, from cannibalism to the Sacraments.

Pigs were kept by prehistoric and predynastic peoples in the Egyptian delta as food animals and for sacrifice to their gods. When upper Egypt conquered lower Egypt, the conquerors regarded these practices with horror. Some Egyptologists tell us that swine were regarded as unclean because the Delta folk ate them. A strict prohibition against swine was then founded on a divine myth: the physical embodiment of Seth, the enemy of Horus.[40] Swineherds and other low castes were excluded from all religious affairs in Egypt even as late as Herodotus; hence, only priests, pharaohs, and nobles observed the strict prohibition, as so did the Hebrews in Egypt under Joseph and Moses. These Egyptian nabobs also abhorred fish, and their heiroglyph for "abomination" was the outline of a fish. When early Christians in Rome and Alexandria clashed with the Isis and other Egyptian cults, they proudly made the sign of the fish of Galilee, not the cross. The cross became the symbol of Christianity later in Christendom.

The pork taboo of Jews and Muslims served the Italian Venetians—good Christians when not engaged in commerce—in an important way. In 828 A.D., according to their own accounts, they stole the body of St. Mark who was martyred in 62 A.D. for protesting the worship of Serapis in Alexandria. The site of his tomb may have been east of Silsileh near the sea where the present Franciscan Church of the Docks now is located in Alexandria. In order to fool the Muslim officials, the wily Venetians placed St. Mark's body in a barrel of pickled hams and pork. No Arab would or could overhaul this noxious and forbidden pig flesh, and thus they were not aware of the robbery for which no payment was made. But St. Mark and his Church and Square in Venice have attracted tourists and pigeons ever since. The pious theft paid off.

In sharp contrast to our modern swine husbandry, the Egyptian delta pig raising left much to be desired. Even as late as 1878, McCoan[41] had the following to say about Egyptian pigs:

---

[40]Kees, Hermann: *Ancient Egypt*. Chicago, University of Chicago Press, 1961, p. 91.

[41]McCoan, J. C.: *Egypt*. New York, P. F. Collier Co., 1878, p. 324.

The *pig* in Egypt is as 'unclean' to all delicate-stomached Christians as to the Moslem or the Jew. It divides with the dog and the kite the scavengering of the towns, and what even the *kelb* refuses as too filthy to be eaten, the *khanzir* ravenously devours. In this respect, 3,500 years—when, in the 18th dynasty, the animal first appears in the sculptures— have but little improved either its habits or its local repute as an article of food. 'As well,' says a recent writer, 'might you dine on a rat taken from a sewer or a vulture caught in the ribbed cavity of a camel it was busy eviscerating. It were all one to sup with the ghools.' No chemistry of nature can, in fact, transmute the filth on which the Egyptian pig generally feeds into fit nutriment for man; and even the least nice of foreign tourists, therefore, will do well to avoid pork at a Cairene *table d'hote*. It is chiefly killed and offered for sale by Greek butchers, whose coreligionists do not so generally share the prejudice which the Copts feel quite as strongly as either Arabs or Jews to the flesh of this animal.

The fear and taboo of pork by north and west Semites originated in their dim past when they were coalescing seminomadic tribes of Arabian peoples, before emerging as 'Apiru-Hebrews, Akkadians, Canaanites-Phoenicians, etc. When barbecuing their sacrificial pigs to their various gods and eating these inadequately cooked and often trichinous tissues (the parasite is killed at 137° F.), high morbidity and mortality rates resulted. These Semitic cultural groups were first chastened with the gods' displeasure and the keener survivors soon reasoned that the terror was associated with the pigs—not their gods. The pig became taboo for Jews and Muslims and has remained so ever since. Today trichinae in carnivorous animals is world-wide, even holoarctic (in white whale, bear, foxes, walrus, seal and dog[42]).

The ancient Semites, Talmudic doctors, and Mohamet knew nothing about the cause of trichinosis, a discovery which could only be made when the microscope came into use. Obviously the pig furnishes no ready by-products: no wool, no milk, no motive power. They are hard to drove and must live chiefly in oak forests or beech woodlands, foraging and rooting for

---

[42]Connell, F. H.: Trichinosis in the Arctic. *Arctic* 2:98-107, 1949.

acorns, beechnuts and fungi (truffles). In historic time, there were no great forests or woodlands in these areas for them. Also, a pig eats more than several men. So there was a lack of food for hogs in the Middle East after the protohistoric period. There was no waste food. The terrain could not support pigs after the dearth of forests. Olive, almond, and fruit trees do not supply food or places for these animals to graze and root. If a man owned large numbers of animals, his ostentation created disturbances. Pork spoils rapidly (15% fat in lean loins) in hot climates. Eventually, vegetation and sapling-destroying goats and sheep took their place, for the terrain was generally poor, and soil attrition then proceeded down the ages. (Camels came in much later to hasten this process).

Food tabus (taboos) are often shown to be a result of many factors and among these are the factors of food poisoning, either bacterial or poisons native to plant or animal kingdoms. Allergies, too, are suspect. These factors are documented subjects[42] and need no further discussion here except to point out that in the distant past of peoples, the illnesses may have been limited to or included a military leader, important priest or shaman, or other personage who if he survived or at the agonal period might have issued a decree. Larger outbreaks among the people—sporadically enough to designate the peccant food or foods—are more often the genesis of food taboos which in the pre-scientific ages would be clothed with ritualistic or religious facets. Also, in order to maintain integrity (segregation) of a people, historians of foods and nutrition tell us, erection of vertical bars of food taboos can effectively accomplish this result if maintained over a long period with religious acceptance.

In Leviticus and Deuteronomy, the Code of Moses deals with these restrictions, but many of the food practices of the Tigris-Euphrates valley and Ugarit of Phoenician Syria were introduced previously by the groups of Abraham. The food regulations or the Kosher Code of Judaism, according to E. J. Goodspeed of the University of Chicago, were one of several

---

[42a]Jensen, L. B.: *Man's Foods.* Champaign, Garrard Press, 1953, pp. 197-198.

main safeguards against assimilation to gentiles. To this day, the Abyssinian Christian Church (of the Lion of Judah) bans the eating of pork.

Nelson Gluek, the famous Jewish-American archeologist of Palestine (Israel), in a lecture November 10, 1939, told of being entertained that year in the tent of an important sheikh in Jordan. The chief dish was a kid that had been boiled in its mother's milk. This ancient ritual was practiced in Ras Shamra or Ugarit (4000-1200 B.C.), and in temples of Mesopotamia (from whence came Abraham) some 5,000 years ago. This local sheikh had never heard that the practice was forbidden to Israelites over 3,100 years ago (Exodus, chapters 19, 23, 26, 34). Also milk and dairy products were not to be eaten with meats.

Abraham and his people before him in Mesopotamia, Syria, and Phoenicia had experienced and rejected many of these early rituals of Neolithic inspiration arising in protoliterate times. The excavated libraries of Ugarit (4000 to 1200 B.C.) tell us all about this custom and the antecedents of early Hebrew beliefs, songs, and psalms which long afterwards were incorporated in the Old Testament. These religious texts of Ugarit prove conclusively that there was great opposition with which the Mosaic tradition had to contend in the well-organized and elaborate religious environments of Baal, El, Astarte, and other rituals of the times.

Since water was scarce and some sources not very palatable in Palestine, a good deal of milk of sheep or goats was drunk but usually as soured milk. Curds and cheese were made (Proverbs 30:33, I Sam. 17:18). When Israel's children of the Exodus first beheld Canaan, they termed it a "land of milk and honey." To the modern agricultural scientist, this means a fairly unproductive soil for grain, since honeybees, blossoms and herd or grazing animals do not provide sufficient food surpluses like the irrigated fields of the Nile and old Mesopotamia. Of course, there were some good grain crop-bearing soils in Palestine, and both Canaanites and Hebrews made excellent use of them, as the Israelis do today.

Under the Pharisees, much was also done to alter the Biblical laws governing dietary and culinary habits and procedures. These Hebrew priestly laws encompassed the millennium-old prohibition about eating meat and milk at the same meal. African primitives of today, whose diet is regulated on this score the very same way, believe that a sacrificial kid or lamb, if eaten in its mother's milk, will dry the milk glands of women and beasts. But the prophets, doctors of the law, and rabbis did not dream of this irrational explanation. They believed the admonition or law was of divine origin and elaborated it so that taboo was extended to forbid any meat or any milk products (milk, cream, cheese, curds, butter), to be eaten together in any household. Further, the plates and culinary utensils, water and washcloths could not be used in combined cleaning from meat meals and dairy meals. A prescribed length of time must elapse before using meat after milk had been drunk. These restrictions were vertical bars of self-imposed segregation for the "spiritual" health of the people, not perhaps a matter of hygiene and health. The taboos of the Hindu caste system are another extreme example of this segregation.

The Near East shares with the rest of the earth's peoples gastrointestinal infections and intoxications owing to specific bacteria, viruses, and parasites. It has been our observations that occidental visitors in the areas of the Fertile Crescent have their bouts with the "gypies," "tourista," "green apple quick-step," and near-fatal, and occasionally fatal, episodes of food poisoning and infections. Infectious microorganisms have selected mankind since the first "new masses" of the first cities and towns of millennia ago segregated in innocent squalor of the nuclear Near East.

The virulent *Shigella* (dysentery group), *Salmonella* (typhoid and paratyphoid groups—over 1,000 serotypes now known), *Streptococci*, and *Paracolon* groups all exact their toll in morbidity and mortality. The toxin formers, the 80 per cent lethal *C. botulinum* and widespread, but not often lethal, enterotoxic *Staphylococci* are bad actors everywhere, but *S. aureus* and some *S. albus* can immobilize anyone to undignified postures— even the Sudanese army several years ago. Hardly anyone who has been examined by laboratory methods in the Near East fails to show parasitical intestinal infections and the carrier-condition for virulent enterobacteria. But 8,000 years of collective living has resulted in degrees of immunity in these people without, however, in many cases, any great degree of buoyant health. Eosinophilia of the blood, denoting parasitical infestation, is a routine finding which correlates with further laboratory examinations. The fossilized feces found in 9,000-year-old sites show pinworms and ova of intestinal parasites.

One facet of kosher preparation of meats has intrigued the present writer. The Jews always trimmed out the large blood vessels of the forequarters of beef. Blood and clots remaining in these vessels may harbor bacteria introduced by the knife of the "schackter," and in addition, the uracil of the blood-vessel lining seems to enhance toxin formation of enterotoxic staphylococci when grown in uracil media or in ground-up blood vessels. (Further work could be done on this aspect of enterotoxin production).

Brucellosis, a dreary disease once called Malta fever (St. Paul when shipwrecked on Malta may have "cured" many Maltese of this disease), is of worldwide distribution and is discerned here in the Near East and Mediterranean littoral in deep antiquity. Three varieties of these bacteria may infect all mammals, wild or domesticated, (*Brucella suis* of pigs, *B. melitensis* of goats, and *B. abortus* of cattle), but each genera of mammal may harbor a specific kind, i.e. the porcine, the caprine, and the bovine. Often a kid or calf is aborted from the infected mother. Thoroughly boiling the kid in the colostral milk would kill these bacteria. But insufficient culinary heating does not destroy the *Brucella* in the kid's deeper tissues.

We shall add something more to this somber facet of public health. The ancient (and modern) custom of providing market meats in these lands, as well as in some other hot regions of the new and Old Worlds, evolved before the sanitary sciences and technologies were vouchsafed us in very recent times by patient, hard-working microbiologists and sanitary engineers. The food animal is killed in early morning, and the meats must be sold before the sun sets that day. Naturally, without refrigeration, the meat spoils through microbial action and rapidly becomes fly-blown. Upon microbiologic examination of these meats in public stalls of the Near East, it is regularly observed that the numbers of bacteria reach huge figures—many millions per gram with warmth and time for incubation. Among the genera and species of these microorganisms, we find many food-poisoning types mentioned above. *Thorough cooking* of these meats will kill these bacteria and nullify the toxins (four types) of *C. botulinum* and also kill the numerous parasites, but the toxin of staphylococci is not destroyed after many hours in boiling water. We showed that upon controlled inoculations into the meats (and other nonacid foods containing over 30% moisture) with known toxin-forming staphylococci, enough of the toxin or food poison developed in five hours in the temperature range of 75° to 110° F. to make human volunteers very ill upon ingestion of the test foods. (The Near East provides good incubation temperatures.)

Viral hepatitis is common in these lands, the New World, and temperate Europe. The two types of hepatic viruses are not killed by boiling in water for four hours! These viruses are present in the domestic-sewage cycle, and infections are spread through ingestion of any infected food and drink, from man to man, and more seriously by transfusions of blood and infected plasma and needles. Plastic syringes with attached needles, quite inexpensive, are now available and are discarded after individual use.

Allah protects the epidemiologists and hardy archeologists in the Fertile Crescent lands, but, of course, there is little protection from the psychosomatic illnesses resulting from chronic lack of funds for their important work.

While there is little immediate prospect or possibility for pork-eating by the Muslims, Jews, Copts, and Abyssinians, the Western World, with the aid of science and technology, has learned to produce safe pork foods. Beginnning with "nonparasitical hog-feeding methods," culinary-heat treatments, and freezing, the larval stage of the trichina worm encysted in muscle tissues of the pig can be controlled. Numerous tests over the years have shown that the larvae are killed when heated to 132° F. Official requirements call for 137° F or higher in every portion of the tissues. Freezing technologies demanded by the Federal Meat Inspection Division have long been in use to insure killing of this parasite. (We also aided in many tests conducted by the Federal scientists on this problem).

The raw meat pieces held at 36° to 38° F are divided into two groups. Group I comprises meat not more than six inches in depth; group II comprises pieces exceeding six inches but not exceeding twenty-seven inches. Freezing time and temperatures then follow this regulation:

Temp.	Group I	Group II
5° F	20 days	30 days
−10° F	10 days	20 days
−20° F	6 days	12 days

There are many regulations involving curing pork products with salt, nitrates and nitrites, drying, smoking procedures, etc., which provide safety for persons eating these foods. Space does not permit further descriptions, and furthermore, the Federal Meat Inspection Division regulations are rigidly enforced to the letter on the spot by their officers and inspectors.

Over a span of more than a quarter of a century, we investigated many cases of trichinosis as an epidemiologist, laboratory analyst, and medicolegal specialist. A few cases tried in Federal, state, circuit and county courts may suffice to illustrate points in this turbulent field.

In one trial, testimony brought out that the plaintiff—a male high school athlete—had heard that his vigor and prowess might be enhanced if he ate raw meat. Thereupon by stealth in his home at night he would come downstairs to the refrigerator and devour raw pork sausage. Repeating this practice over a period of time he developed severe trichinosis. Later on, the lad's father sued the retailer and purveyor. Biopsy of muscle at the insertion of the deltoid muscle (a relatively painless procedure employing a small surgical hook) revealed calcified encysted larvae setting his illness further back in time than his allegations (hospital record). Neither the court nor jury heeded this fact and found for the plaintiff, albeit the damages were less than nominal, i.e. $100.00. (The boy had actually eaten many brands of raw pork sausage!)

Three additional cases coming to trial were brought by some Italian people who prepared a staple old-country cured-spiced pork sausage stuffed in casings and cured at room temperature for 2 to 3 weeks in their homes. (In Italy, pigs are rarely parasitized because there are no leftover raw-meat scraps fed to them). After eating these home-cured sausages, classical trichinosis ensued. The defendant companies won in these cases, but the law at that time was unclear because of the celebrated "metwurst-brockwurst" litigation in Ohio many years ago. In this case, an unheated sausage caused trichinosis (the small sausage kitchen where the product was made did not observe the freezing regulations). The fresh pork was dressed and sold by a meat packer. The trial record went up and down the apellate and trial courts several times because of difficulty in affixing "legal blame."

Since many persons (the older age groups, ethnic groups, and certain rural populations) harbor encysted larvae over their life span after infestation, the biopsy material may be misleading for diagnostic and trial purposes. Also plaintiffs' testimony, influenced by the dream of sudden riches, described the culinary treatment of the raw pork purchased from a solvent company to have been more than adequate ("almost burnt to a cinder").

In two other trials of cases where the plaintiffs ate their own prepared sausage incubated at room temperature for two to three weeks, we observed Staphylococcus enterointoxication. In this family outbreak, only two of eight persons at risk developed trichinosis—the parasite being largely eliminated by vomiting and diarrhea. In one Connecticut family outbreak alpha streptococci (Lancefield's group D, i.e. *S. fecalis* and *S. faecium*) caused diarrhea in eight to fifteen hours, and three of six persons at risk presumably developed trichinosis from eating their own prepared sausage. The trichina, male and the female, did not reach maturity in order for the female to lodge in the intestinal wall, and discharge larvae.

To illustrate the attitude of judges of yesteryear who had to hear these lawsuits, we quote Judge Woodward who wrote "the celebrated medicolegal ballad" during a recess in a trichinosis trial about 50 years ago:

Encapsulated in a hog, a tiny microbe lay,
His parents had departed by the alimentary way.
The hog was one of many
And the microbe one of more,
But one day opportunity came knocking at the door.

Now every hog, like every dog, is said to have his day,
And to our hog it came as in the western mire it lay.
They took him from his happy home
His father and his mother;
They hung him up and slit his throat from one ear to the other.
They cut his body into parts for government inspection
For fear of trichinosis or other chance infection,
And all the while this microbe
Lay safe within his cyst
Assured that without microscopic inspection he'd be missed.

The hog was shipped to Nanticoke beside the Susquehanna,
And sold to some Italians named Catani and Tavana.
They took it from its package,
And they chose to eat it fried,
And thereafter all brought lawsuits excepting those who died.

For the little worm got angry when in the frying pan
And vowed if he got out of that alive he'd enter man.
And with a mighty struggle,
He burst forth from his shell,
And proceeded in Catani and Tavana to raise merry Hell.

And now in Luzerne County not a single term goes by
But someone of the judges has a microbe case to try.
One came before Judge Fuller,
And one before O'Boyle.
Judge Strauss had one, and Woodward has just begun his toil.

The judge's knowledge of parasitology left something to be desired, but his attitude showed alertness, together with lyrical poesy and a fine judicial temperament. Microscopic inspection was abandoned in 1906 as being impractical and too costly, and as giving the consumer a false sense of security.

One of the most useful discussions on all phases of trichinosis, both scientific and legal, for the practical hygienist is to be found in A. R. Miller's *Meat Hygiene*.[43] Miller, before retirement several years ago, was Chief of the Federal Meat Inspection Service, U.S.D.A., Washington, D.C., and had long experience in this field. As this is written, nothing which we might say can be added to the subject in all of its scientific and legal aspects so ably treated by Dr. Miller.

---

[43]Miller, A. R.: *Meat Hygiene*. Philadelphia, Lea & Febiger, 1951, pp. 81-104.

INHERENT TOXICITY OF NATURAL
PRODUCTS MISTAKENLY USED
AS FOODS

WE SHALL DEAL briefly here with recent or current natural toxic products complicating the picture of food poisoning.

The effects of unspoiled poisonous fish of tropical and subtropical waters have long been under observation in the South Pacific, Japan, Philippines, Hawaii, West Indies, and elsewhere.[44-49] Recently, physicians have been alerted to the dangers of eating poisonous species of fish where they are caught or when shipped frozen to other parts of the country.[50] The species implicated are barracuda, red snapper, herring, pompano, sea bass, perch, moonfish, horse mackerel, tuna, and bonito. It is noteworthy that most of these fish are highly toxic only at certain times of the year. It is believed that the poisons are derived from the diet of the fish, but more knowledge is needed about the chemical and pharmacologic properties of the toxins, as well as the dietary origin and distribution of the poisons in the tissues of the fish. Onset of symptoms occurs within a few minutes to several hours, and in severe form, the fatality rate may reach 60 per cent. Symptoms are nausea, vomiting, flush-

---

[44]Dack, G. M.: *Food Poisoning.* 3rd ed. Chicago, University of Chicago Press, 1956, 229-233.

[45]Meyer, K. F.: Food poisoning. *New Eng. J. Med. 249*:765-812, 1954.

[46]Dewberry, E. B.: *Food Poisoning.* 3rd ed. Leonard Hill, 1950.

[47]Jordan, E. O.: *Food Poisoning and Food-Borne Infection.* Chicago, University of Chicago Press, 1931, 154-155.

[48]Halstead, B. W.: Poisonous fish—A medical-military problem. *Res. Rev.,* O. N. R., Dept. of Navy, pp. 10-16, *Copeia,* No. 1, 31-33, 1953.

[49]Tanner, F. W. and Tanner, L. P.: *Food-Borne Infections and Intoxications.* Champaign, Garrard Press, 1953, 119-129.

[50]Editorial: Poisonous fish. *J. A. M. A., 163*:118-119, 1957.

ing, giant urticaria, headache, respiratory distress, and cyanosis of lips, tongue, and gums. Shellfish poisoning was recognized in 1793 by Captain Vancouver on the Pacific Coast,[51] and occurs on the northern Atlantic Coast.[52] Many primitive economies have been seriously dislocated by eating poisonous shellfish.

Meyer, Somer, and colleagues[53] of the Hooper Foundation, University of California, during the past thirty years have studied 409 cases of mussel or clam poisoning occurring from Juneau, Alaska to southern California. There is, however, worldwide distribution of shellfish poisoning. The mussels feed on plankton (Gonyaulax catenella), producing "red water" in daylight and luminescence at night. The poison found in these dinoflagellates is one of the strongest known and acts like the alkaloids belonging to the aconitine-muscarine-strychnine class. Some of its chemical properties are now known, thanks to the technics of ion exchange and chromatography, although the exact chemical structure remains to be determined. For practical assay, mouse units are determined by injection and results expressed in units/50 gm of mussel livers and syphons. When canned clams are assayed, 100 gm of ground clam meats are used. The mouse unit is defined as that amount of mussell poison which, when dissolved in 1 ml of water and injected intraperitoneally into a 20 gm white mouse, will cause death in fifteen minutes. Color tests and quantitative chemical methods are now available. The symptoms are respiratory paralysis, numbness of lips, tingling of fingertips, giddiness, then staggering and drowsiness, sensations of gripping and dryness of throat. Reflexes or heart rate are not affected. Death from respiratory failure may occur quickly, but if patient survives twelve hours, the prognosis is good. The mortality rate has been about 9 per cent. Meyer found no significant changes at autopsy.

---

[51]Furk, D. M.: *Shellfish Poisoning.* Report 82. Fisheries Research Board of Canada, Vancouver, B. C., 1950.

[52]Medcof, J. C., Gibbard, J. *et al.*: *Paralytic Shellfish Poisoning on the Canadian Atlantic Coast. Fisheries* Research Board of Canada, Ottawa, Bulletin 75, 1947.

[53]Meyer, K. F.: Food poisoning. *New Eng. J. Med., 249:*765-812, 1954.

There are additional kinds of poisonous marine and fresh water animals like the asari oyster of Japan, poisonous shark livers, roe and gonads of minnows of freshwater European barbel, and moray eels, none of which will be dealt with in this discussion, since these poisonings are probably not of significant occurrence in this country.

In recent years, in distinction from the past, poisonous plants have not contributed significantly to the food-poisoning picture. One of the old offenders is rhubarb greens which, upon ingestion, produce vomiting, cramping, diarrhea, no elevation of temperature in some instances but rapid rise in other cases, cloudy urine, failure of blood to clot, and in fatal cases, slow onset (sometimes thirty hours) of rigor mortis, The rhubarb leaves may contain 0.4 per cent of oxalic acid. Other oxalic acid-containing vegetation which have infrequently caused poisoning are sour grass-sorrel in soups, beet leaves used as "greens," and wild grapes *(Ampelopsis quinquefolia)*.

Poisonings, usually in children, have resulted from their eating poisonous plants, seeds, and deceptive berries. For example, berries of bittersweet *(Solanum dulcamara)* or berries of the deadly nightshade *(Atropa belladonna)* have caused death. Also, children mistaking shoots of the mountain laurel *(Kalmia latifolia)* for wintergreen have been severely poisoned. The castor bean used as a cathartic or given to youngsters to play with has been eaten with fatalities from the toxic and allergy-like action of both the ricin and oil (discussed under "Castor Oil" in Part II.) Tung nuts and nutmegs have also caused poisoning. The black locust containing the extremely poisonous robin; roots of the water hemlock ("cowbane") confused with wild parsnip; water hemlock *(Circuta)* growing in wet places, widely distributed in the United States and mistaken by children for horseradish, have all caused illness and death, although the incidence of cases is not great.

Potato poisoning ("solanine poisoning") was once thought to be rife, especially from eating green potatoes. Khan[54] has

---

[54]Khan, P.: *A Study of Outbreaks of Food Poisoning Alleged to Be Due to Poisonous Potatoes. Thesis,* The University of Chicago, 1949.

reviewed the literature and found that this entity is not tenable; bacterial agencies, not the glucoalkaloid could be involved if potatoes were at all in the case. One would have to eat 16.6 lb. of potatoes containing solanine to develop symptoms of poisoning.

II
Vegetal and Mineral
Poisons

INTRODUCTION

In these sections, we list some of the poisons of the Ancient World and outline a few of our own encounters with the forensic problems in this field while a partner in the Chicago Laboratory with Dr. R. W. Webster, Coroner's Chemist and Professor of Toxicology and Medical Jurisprudence at Rush Medical College. Our medicolegal work in this field over the years was continued in other laboratories and for several agencies. Most of our notes in the sections to follow are obviously not intended to exhaust the subjects. The literature in this field of toxicology and history could, indeed, be voluminous and would require an old-style German "Handbuch" to encompass source materials and secondary works. We have, in certain sections, noted only excerpts of recorded events in the past not available in modern treatises known to us.

Poisoning with criminal intent has always intrigued scientists, physicians, pharmacists, lawyers, law enforcing officers, and detective-story writers. This murder by stealth is an ancient practice. Having been engaged in forensic-laboratory analyses and an expert witness in trials of cases where those accused of poisoning were in the "docks" of criminal courts as defendants, we noted over the years many facets of this area of human (or inhuman) conduct.

Most of us, when we were beginners in forensic chemistry fifty years ago, felt quite satisfied with our dexterity in employing the Marsh and Gutzeit tests for arsenic and other tests for chemicals of the qualitative chemical tables. When we progressed to alkaloid detection, we had supposedly reached the top. Perusal of the then-current literature and textbooks on toxicology and legal medicine soon nullified our vanity. For some reason, this field of inquiry remained fairly static from about 1920 to 1950. Then a new departure ensued, mainly through the efforts of "LD_{50} pharmacologists," and "animal-feeding nutritionists," formerly physiologists. This situation was brought into focus during the bread hearings in Washington, D. C. (1949-1952) and continued during the food-additives hearings which followed. Singularly enough, these experts disdained the voluminous data preceding 1939. They employed white rats in their work, whereas their predecessors observed another type of rat in their work, i.e. the criminal. The great hiatus resulting from their slogan, typical of the times, "don't go back more than ten years—nothing of value can be had in the preceding literature," led to much political, commercial, governmental, and academic sounds of fury. Each "Virchow" protested when his data from acute tests and two-year rat-feeding tests were equivocal, especially the gross and microscopic pathology interpretations. (A good pathologist and toxicologist in this area spends decades acquiring proficiency).

Two simple questions often asked (quickly) in trials and hearings served to point up a pseudopathologist: "Does a rat have a gall bladder?" and "Can a rabbit vomit?" The true response in both cases is "no!" The rat does not possess a gall bladder and the rabbit cannot vomit.

We recall one example of each response. A self-styled expert, who testified (under oath) that he had personally "autopsied over ten thousand white rats," was not sure about the rats' gall bladders showing pathologic changes. The other man was a self-styled pathologist who testified under oath that his test rabbits possessed vomiting centers and "vomited profusely" when fed the material under litigation. To be sure, none of us is perfect. Perhaps, under oath and stress proper words fall out of a Byzantine vocabulary.

POISONS IN THE GRECO-ROMAN WORLD

Because poisoning with criminal intent has obviously been a clandestine art throughout recorded ancient history, precise information is not usually available in the records that have come down to us. Ancient writers, Tacitus for example, mention these criminal acts with great regularity, but a modern student of toxicology and paleopathology must often infer from ancillary evidence the nature of the agent and the poisons available to the ancient poisoners.

Classical physicians and philosophers rarely mention these matters. Hippocrates, Herophilus, Galen, and the compilers of medical treatises of Egypt, Mesopotamia, Syria-Palestine, Greece, and Rome were healers, and for the most part very ethical men for their age, as one surmises from Hippocrates' oath for physicians. (Hippocrates' genuine works contain no information about criminal poisoning).

We know from the studies of Hans Zinsser[55] on infectious diseases in ancient times that the etiologies of epidemics, malnutrition, infectious disease entities, mental pathology, and perhaps ingestion of some toxic agents were then often impossible to diagnose. While disease was thought to be largely the work of gods and demons, in lieu of exact knowledge, it is to the credit of Hippocrates, Dioscorides, Herophilus, Galen, and others that they had the true scientific outlook if not the methodologies. Hippocrates did use laudanum of the white poppy and helleborin which acts on the central nervous system to relieve pain. Overdoses of both paralyze the central nervous system.

In Neolithic or early food-producing times, the ceramic technologies of cooking pots (and later, copper, bronze, and iron swinging cauldrons, pots and pans, and glassware) came into general use in the Fertile Crescent, India, China, and Mediter-

---

[55]Zinsser, H.: *Rats, Lice and History.* Boston, Little, Brown, 1935.

ranean areas, thus facilitating the preparation of poisonous infusions from plants, soluble minerals like the oxides of arsenic,
concentrated toadstool or toxic mushroom extracts and powders,
toxic alkaloids, and other poisons to be dealt with later in this
survey.

The original habitat of poisonous plants and the centers of
origin of both cultivated and indigenous vegetation are now
fairly well documented through the travels and genetic researches of Vavilov, a martyr of genetics.[55a] This trustworthy source
provides the information, in part, of the vegetal poisons available through trade and primary and secondary origins. Treatises
on pharmaceutical botany like those of Theophrastus, also provide some information from antiquity. A partial list of poisonous
plants of enough importance to be cultivated in their early
habitats were:

> India: *Cannabis indica* and *sativa,* "pot", or mari-
> huana (hemp, hasheesh)
> *Croton tiglium* (croton oil, a powerful
> purge)
> *Strychnos nux-vomica* (strychnine nut)
>
> Near East
> and elsewhere: *Papaver somniferum* (opium, morphine)
> Castor bean, (ricin, a toxin) (ricinine, an
> alkaloid)
> Rhubarb (leaves very toxic—oxalic acid)
> Hellebore
> Hemlock
> Aconite

The soluble, toxic, mineral poisons available to ancient poisoners were not many in number, but arsenic, lead, and antimony salts were used with criminal intent then as in the Western World up to the nineteenth and early twentieth century.

[55a]Vavilov, N. I.: *The Origin, Variation, Immunity and Breeding of Cultivated
Plants. Chronica Botanica, 13,* 1950. (Professor Vavilov disappeared and was
thought to have been executed by Stalin).

Aside from the acts of frank professional poisoners in the Greco-Roman world, the fear of death by poison gave rise in ruling or aristocratic circles to the professions of cupbearer, king's tasters, and trusted patrician's chefs. The chef of a great household in Imperial Rome, for instance, was a great personage when fully trusted, and chefs were so powerful in certain reigns that the Roman Market Police, if they tried to enforce the food laws, were turned over by the patrician to his chef and cooks for rough handling.[56] In an earlier age, Xenophon (400 B.C.) remarks that addition of poison to food and drink was so common among the Medes that it was absolutely necessary for the cupbearer to taste food and wine before it was offered to the King.[57]

Tacitus's *Annals of Imperial Rome* deal often with assassination by poisons. Very little mention is ever made of the type of agent employed, and little information is given about symptoms and *modus operandi* which is, of course, now the business of forensic science in this modern scientific age.

In book 1.4 (14 A.D.), Tacitus records that Augustus was slowly poisoned by his wife Livia. In his book 11.85 (19 A.D.), Tacitus states that a German Chatti chief named Adgandestrius wrote the senate that he would kill the Teutonic hero, Arminius[58] if poison were sent him for the job. "The reported

---

[56] Jensen, L. B.: *Meat and Meat Foods.* New York, Ronald Press, 1949, p. 182 ff.

[57] The kings of the Medes and Persians grew so apprehensive of poisoners that they overreacted (to use the modern word) in dealing with the problem. An excerpt from the life of Artaxerxes, king of Persia, outlines the judicial punishment for this crime. The poisoners were layed between two troughs with their face uncovered and bedaubed with honey to attract wasps, hornets, bees, and biting flies. They were force-fed milk, to prolong the torment, which if refused, the king's men ran needles into the poisoner's eyes most persuasively, and left them until the vermin ate them up!

[58] Quincitilius Varus, legate of the Rhine army, penetrating the German forests collecting tribute and enslaving the unwary, was attacked by the Cherusci under the youthful Arminius (Herman, Armand) in the Teutoburg forest in 9 A.D. where he perished with 21,000 of his legionnaires. Caesar Augustus was often heard to cry: "Varus give me back my Legions," and abandoned the Elbe frontier. Herman, however, died at the age of thirty-seven from poison given him by a treacherous kinsman (another version says "slain").

answer was that Romans take vengeance on their enemies, not by underhand tricks, but by open force of arms. By this elevated sentiment, Tiberius invited comparisons with generals of old who had forbidden and disclosed the plan to poison King Pyrrhus." Apparently, the Germanic tribes did not possess "poisons," but the Celtiberians and Gauls did, as we shall see later on.

The profession of poisoner is illustrated by a reference in Tacitus, Book 111.2, "The notorious poisoner, Martina, sent to Rome by Cnaeus Sentius Saturnius had suddenly died at Brundusium; and that, although her body bore no signs of suicide, poison had been found hidden in a knot of her hair."

Tacitus writes much of Sejanus, Tiberius' confidant. Apparently, Sejanus was an accomplished poisoner, and killed many people who were in his way to power. It is again interesting to note that in trials, various aristocrats were accused of inflicting death by use of both poison and spells. One wonders about the fate of Sejanus. There is a gap of two years in the manuscript of Tacitus, but other historians record that Tiberius had Sejanus executed. Sejanus' divorced wife revealed to the Emperor that his own son Drusus had been poisoned by Sejanus and Empress Livilla. Livilla was then executed. "Several empresses who were not devoted or virtuous wives injected oysters with deadly poisons (not named) as agreeable agents for administering death to their husbands and lovers of whom they tired."

These are just a few of the many examples of criminality in Imperial Rome that we found in our quest to discover the toxic agents and some Roman toxicology and methods.

In the Near East of Hellenistic and Roman times, criminal poisonings were the order of the day, and poisoning with venoms, chemicals, alkaloids, and other vegetal extracts to be discussed, became a science in Syria, Palestine and Alexandrian Egypt. Slaves, war captives, and dogs were used to test poisons for kind, reaction, and potency. For instance, Cleopatra used slaves for testing asp venom, strichnine, and other poisons to determine the ease of death.

Most of the physicians of Hellenistic and Roman times were trained in Alexandria or the great cities of Asia Minor, as well as in Greece and Cos. Some of these men were of criminal mind, but the majority of them practiced the arts of medicine and surgery in the finest tradition of Hippocrates. A large part of the physicians' drug collection was, however, made up of antidotes for poisons. Everyone dreaded being poisoned. Many peculiar deaths due to "natural" illnesses were charged up to toxic drugs. The Hellenistic and Roman physicians could dull pain, induce sleep by use of atropin (*Mandragora*), and operate for cataract by distending the eyepupil by use of *Anagallis*. There were many shops selling crude drugs in Rome and the large cities of the Empire, but no regular prescription pharmacists are known from the literary records. However, the celebrated wall paintings of Pompeii depict pharmacists at work.

Josephus tells us of the vicious Palestinean kinglets—Herod, Antipater, *et al.*—in their dynastic quarrels and repeated trips to Rome for assistance and who were always plotting assassination by poison or dagger of those in their way. "Pheroras, Herod's brother, supped with his wife the day before he fell sick. . . .A certain potion was brought him in such a sort of food as he was not used to eat; but that when he had eaten, he died of it; that this potion was brought out of Arabia by a woman under pretense indeed as a love-potion, for that was its name, but in reality to kill Pheroras; for that the Arabian women are skillful in making such poisons. . . . The woman confessed to others . . . both Pheroras' wife's mother and sister had procured the poison from her. Their women slaves were put to torture and all was discovered." Another version was that Antiphilus brought the poison out of Egypt through his brother, a physician, and it was meant for Herod himself. "The poison was burned—the largest part of it—and it was contained in a box. The Jewish Roman delegation now returned with more poison to insure Herod's death, but were unsuccessful." The accounts of Josephus are very involved. The Egyptian poison must have been of vegetal origin or it would not "burn."

The physicians of Cos, Hippocrates among them, and later Hellenistic-Roman physicians used *Mandragora* for eye surgery, as well as for alleviation of pain and for local anesthesia. The plant, according to Freya Stark (*Ionia, a Quest*. New York, Harcourt, Brace, 1955, p. 49), grows only on Chios, in Palestine; in Tibet and in Cyprus. This plant belongs to the *Solanaceae (Mandragora officinalis)*, and the roots contain the alkaloid ($C_{15}H_{19}O_2N$). The drug is brown, amorphous, and acts like atropine (Merck's Index). Overdoses are lethal, and most probably, this drug was used as a poison in ancient times.

On Cos at the altar of Asclepius and Apollo the Oath of Hippocrates, which stressed the crime of poisoning, was first pronounced. Strangely enough, Emperor Claudius, because of his trust of Xenophon, his Greek-Coan physician, issued an imperial edict naming all the famous doctors who had practiced at the hospital of Cos from remotest antiquity, and added a eulogy of Xenophon. Xenophon repaid Claudius a few years later by giving him poison. When the Emperor vomited up the poison, Xenophon pretended to help him by inserting a feather in his throat. The feather was soaked in an even more toxic substance, and the Emperor died in agony. To this obscure doctor in an ungrateful world we owe the emergence of Nero, the murderer of St. Peter and St. Paul, according to Christian tradition, and apparently a very disordered person. He was one of many who gave rise to the saying, "Absolute power corrupts absolutely."

The great classical historian of modern times, Miss Edith Hamilton, an honorary citizen of Athens, wrote that Juvenal's world was a nightmare city where no one could drink a cup of wine without fearing poison.[59] In her book on Rome,[60] Miss Hamilton quotes Juvenal and his intense feelings about the times, "a warning to stepsons in general that 'those hot cakes are black with poison of a mother's baking'," and ends with the statement that you will meet, every morning, a woman who has murdered her husband, "no street but has its Clytemnestra." "Agrippina served poisonous mushrooms to her imperial husband." She says also that torturing slaves for confession and

---

[59]Hamilton, Edith: *The Echo of Greece*. New York, Norton, 1957, p. 183.

[60]idem: *The Roman Way to Western Civilization*. New York, Mentor, 1957, pp. 142-157.

mass execution of household slaves for murder by poisons of masters or members of family were upheld by the Roman Senate. "People still whisper stories of that awful poison-vendor, the woman Locusta, who probably supplied Nero's mother, Agrippina, with the fatal powder she sprinkled on her husband Claudius' dish of mushrooms and then another dose to Nero himself to kill his stepbrother, Britannicus, with a highly spiced goblet." (The physician Xenophon is not implicated in this version).

After Galen's time in Rome, the empire declined, and the deterioration of civilization was rapid, as was the deterioration of medicine. Physicians became more and more ignorant, dogmatic, and mercenary. Dealers in magic, professional poisoners, and courtesans who peddled drugs became familiar figures in Rome.

Emperor Elagabalus, when told by a soothsayer that he would die a violent death, prepared worthy means of suicide if occasion required: cords of purple silk, swords of gold, and numerous poisons enclosed in sapphires or emeralds. He was slain in a latrine.[61] Ammianus Marcellinus[62] records Roman life in his day (circa 300-400 A.D.) with poisoners and every kind of depravity rampant. There were, of course, many decent people, both pagan and Christian, in the Roman Empire living up to ethical rules comparable to those of our own turbulent era. Thanks to modern science, detection of known old poisons, new poisons, and the skill in apprehending poisoners has abated this ancient scourge to a minimum. Most laymen are forgetful of this boon to existence vouchsafed them by patient, hard-working toxicologists. However, some criminals in this area do escape detection. Some, when apprehended, escape sentencing.

---

[61]Historia Augusta, Elagabalus, 19-32. Loeb Classical Library; Dio Gassius, *80*: 13; Herodian *4*, 253.

[62]Books 24:10-15; 26:3-5; 28:4,25 ff.

ANTIDOTES FOR POISONS IN
ANCIENT TIMES

An OLD SAYING of Roman lawyers of the forum in imperial times intimated that human goals were tripartite, i.e. the main chance and two "side effects." For instance, a governor of a province must make three fortunes: one to pay his underlings for robbing the provincials, the second to defray expenses for bribes when standing trial in Rome, and the third fortune to keep for personal comforts. Likewise, the hazard of being poisoned by known "unknown enemies" was always imminent. Three measures could be adopted: (1) have a slave "taster", (2) kill the suspected poisoner, or (3) resort to immunity by taking theriac *(Mithridaticum)* and "bezoars."

Bezoar stones were the hair-mucus balls of oxen and other ruminants, and also gallstones from domestic animals. These were either powdered or infused for *per os* administration. Gallstones of cattle are collected by meat packers for Oriental trade where the "remedy" is still used in China, the Near East, and by certain Arabs whose ancestors carried the idea to Europe in medieval times during their conquests in Spain and Italy. Peruvian archaeologists find that pre-Columbian Indians also employed bezoar stones for medical purposes.[63]

Mithridates, king of Pontus in the second century before Christ, was versed in Greek medicine of Hellenistic Alexandria and Greece. His chief experiments were directed towards finding a universal antidote against poisons and snake venoms of all kinds, using slaves as test subjects. His recipe, dicovered in his archives after death, was the well-known *Mithridaticum* which later physicians developed into the celebrated theriac. (It contained sixty-three ingredients, all of which are now known to

---

[63]Mason, J. A.: *Ancient Civilization of Peru.* New York, Pelican, 1961, p. 221.

be worthless.) The main ingredient was the dried flesh of pit vipers and other venomous snakes. Since the snake was immune to its own poison, he reasoned that it could confer immunity. Theriac was a cure-all in the Near East, Mediterranean lands, western Europe, and the Americas until a hundred years ago. Most of the theriac prescriptions contained liberal amounts of opium. An excerpt from an unknown ancient writer states, "If a man has many deadly foes, he is likely to take a potion of the precious theriac daily—because antidotes for so many poisons are carried in the compound. All histories tell how Mithridates of Pontus, that famous adversary of Sulla and Pompeius, used to take antidotes so constantly that he became entirely immune to the venoms prepared by all his enemies." "Symmachus, who has specific medicines for every disease, and theriac—a mixture of sixty-one different substances including dried adders—has antidotes for hemlock, opium, henbane, gypsum, white lead and many obscurer foods of evil . . . "

Over the centuries, the formulae varied greatly, but of the sixty-two ingredients listed in Europe, the mainstays were gentian root, hyssop, clarified butter, nutmeg, Illyrian iris, incense, myrrh, spikenard, balm of Gilead, Dead Sea bitumen, red earth from Lemnos (Herodotus mentions this earth as an antidote against poison), honey, opium, and dried viper flesh.

After vanquishing Mithridates, King of Pontus (53 B.C.), Pompey confiscated the king's medical library where the secret formula was described in detail. The formula passed eventually to Nero's physician, Andromachus, who "improved" it and launched the "antidote" as "theriaca andromachi." Shortly, it was hailed as a cure-all for all diseases and conditions, as well as an antidote for all poisons. Theriaca became the most famous medicine or cure-all ever known, and was widely used from 70 A.D. to 1870 A.D. Alfred the Great used it, as did the Crusaders. The people of the Middle Ages dosed themselves with Theriaca to cure toothache, plague, "leprosy," battle wounds, and so on. They had blind faith in "theriac," that wonderful placebo!

The word "treacle" is derived from teriaca, the "Venetian treacle." No traveler ever dreamed of leaving Venice without the specific. Maritime Venice was the center of the spice trade and exported great quantities of "treacle" and spices. Pious pilgrims to the Holy Land fortified themselves with theriac and prayers.

One can still buy teriaca from a pharmacy in Venice, near the Rialto bridge (1960). This drug store has been dispensing drugs since 1500 A.D. and according to the chemist, has made and sold teriaca since 1603.

Such was the misplaced confidence in theriac. As the first modern scientists said of the alchemists' search for a universal solvent, What vessel could contain it? and now the physicist's query, How can I put antimatter in tanks?

We may read in Mark 16:18 another commentary on the prevalence of poisoners: "They (believers) shall take up serpents; and if they drink any deadly thing, it shall not hurt them; they shall lay hands on the sick, and they shall recover." This was a theriac of another dimension which primal Christians could employ according to their faith. Modern "sectarians of snake-handling cults" do not fare well with venomous bites and often are speeded on their way to the fundamentalist's heaven due, perhaps, to the mentality of snakes and the snake's ignorance of the Nicene Creed.

VOODOO DEATHS

Voodoo may appear to be a bizarre subject in our discussion of criminal poisonings and food poisoning which have to do with ingestion. However, voodoo poison deaths have been recorded throughout history. This practice, instilling fear in a prospective victim, includes a wide psychic arsenal and is by no means ineffective with persons of primitive mentalities. Cannon had much to say about voodoo death,[64] and Caudill[65] describes benign and malignant successes through "psychotherapeutic measures in primitive societies," as does Coon in his well-known *Reader*

---

[64]Cannon, W. B.: Voodoo death. *Amer. Anthropologist XLIV;* 169-181, 1942.

[65]Caudill, W.: In Kroeber, A. L. (Ed.): *Applied Anthropology in Medicine.* Chicago, University of Chicago Press, 1953, p. 773.

in Anthropolgy (sections on African tribal voodoo). Bewitched food and drink were employed, along with pierced effigies and trophies of death.

A bit of effective voodoo practiced in Egypt sometime during 1195-1164 B.C. is recorded by Egyptologists. Rameses III uncovered a harem plot where the conspirators possessed a book from which written spells and directions for constructing waxen figures could exercise magical influence upon the Pharaoh and his supporters, either by debilitating their limbs or by undermining their sense of duty. Rameses showed no mercy to the officials and harem women. "Let their deeds recoil on their heads. As for me who escaped and was saved for eternity, I am of the company of true kings, etc. . . . " (but Rameses did not long survive this plot).

The conspirators were probably buried alive. Sir Gaston Maspero found a mummy at Deir el Bahari, a probable member of this "conspiracy" whose features were horribly distorted from suffocation. Wilson[66] gives an extended resumé of the remarkable record of this conspiracy which actually cost Pharaoh Rameses III his life and records also the posthumous court inquiry, both procedure and findings.

Tacitus in his *Annals* (11.67) describes the voodoo death of Caesar Germanicus, a good man. Germanicus, in 19 A.D., fell ill in Antioch, Syria, believing that Piso had poisoned him. "Examination of the floor and walls of his bedroom revealed remains of human bodies, spells, curses, lead tablets inscribed with the patient's name, charred and bloody ashes, and other malignant objects which are supposed to consign souls to the powers of the tomb. At the same time, his enemy Piso and agents were spying on the sickbed. Germanicus grew alarmed . . . for the prospects of his wife and babies. Apparently, the poisoning was too slow. Piso left for the island of Cos. Germanicus lost strength, making deathbed requests. . . . Some felt that his appearance, short life, and manner of death, like its locality, recalled the

---

[66]Wilson, J. A.: *Burden of Egypt.* Chicago, University of Chicago Press, 1951, p. 267-269.

poison death of Alexander the Great since both . . . succumbed to the treachery of compatriots in a foreign land."

We have here the superstitious touch with malignant spells and voodoo atmosphere of the sickroom which the tribal Negro still fears. The effectiveness of this psychosomatic ordeal varies, but death results often enough, sometimes by combination with slow poisoning. Certain deaths to this day in the Carribean islands and surrounding coastlands of South America, as well as the delta, are attributed to fear of voodoo efficacy, aided no doubt by physical and chemical means. Our only case in this connection about forty years ago, was a large outbreak of *Staphylococcus* food poisoning from a sausage-in-oil jamboree erroneously ascribed to the ill will of a voodoo witch venting her dislikes through this food agency known as "cotton plantation delight." The poor old woman was also stricken and died. The enterotoxin of *S. aureus* was eventually found to have been the poison. The sausages were incubated for several days during the heat of the summer. This case was tried on the theory of negligence, which theory is difficult to prove. Another trial of a case much like this, in the Carolinas, was predicated on the "doctrine of similar instances" which was an old theory of law based on food complaints of any nature—foreign substances, poisoning, and "foods deleterious to health" produced by one company. Any court record showing verdicts for plaintiffs on one food, carried over as a record of negligence in commercial preparation of another entirely distinct food, in another factory or plant. This was the strong point in trials of these "similar instances" cases. Somehow this doctrine of similar instances and voodoo seemed to run parallel in mentality, or at best, "guilt by association."

WINE, MEAD AND BEER IN
ANCIENT TIMES

THERE ARE NOT A FEW historians of foods who believe that the noble grasses—wheats and barleys—were first harvested for fermented drinks, not bread and porridges. Whatever the truth of the matter, "the little leaven that leaveneth the whole lump" had been used in prehistory (but probably not in preceramic times) for beer, mead, wine, and breadmaking. Since the nature of fermentation was not to be known until quite recent times,[67] the alcoholic effects were ascribed to the gods. Prolongued drunkenness was the work of demons which seems likely from descriptions of drinking establishments and their patrons of four thousand years ago in Egypt. Analysts who examined bootleg whiskey during the prohibition era wrote in summary about the better samples tested. "No poisons present except ethanol."

The Greek and Roman *symposium* (i.e. literally in Greek, "drinking together"), the "conversational" dinner where wine was drunk in amounts decreed by the "president" or "king" elected for the evening's entertainment, led to much trouble, especially in Roman times. The Roman in his cups was hard to handle and quite dangerous; the Greek less so, but not always. Mohamet saw enough of their ways, so he prohibited wine and beer drinks (unfortunately, he did not know of whiskey!). Besides, a hangover in the desert and even hot countries is something to reckon with! Carrying bulky wines on caravan routes was not profitable, and drunkenness here, would be disastrous

---

[67] In the days when the noted German chemist Justus von Liebig and the world figure Louis Pasteur were investigating the nature of fermentation, Professor von Liebig made his famous "last words" criticism of Pasteur's data, "Pasteur would have us believe that his yeasts engorged on sugar, became sick therefrom, and came down with a diarrhea of alcohol!" This statement, coupled with another error in soil chemistry, excited sufficient mirth for transposition of the noble name Liebig to "biglie."

for ordinary discipline and meeting sudden attack with suitable planned defense against nomadic raiders. The Arabs are and were very hospitable and generous, which, in case of wines and other alcoholic drinks at dinner, would end up like the warlike Roman's symposium or worse. Wine, too, is of useless transport in a waterless region. As a Sidonian said, "One glass makes a sheep, two glasses make a lion, and three glasses make a monkey!" An ancient Athenian comedian says, "the first cup means health, the second pleasure, the third may produce sleep in a few which the prudent man heeds by going home, the fourth and fifth mean truculence; the sixth, disorder in the streets, the seventh, black and blue eyes, and eighth, arrest by the Scythian police." Aristophanes adds, "and a throbbing headache into the bargain."

Phoenicians and Punics liked strong wine, both from grape juice and raisins fermented with "must" of wine. Some lime was added to neutralize the acidity, thus increasing the ethanol content. The Greeks and Romans decried this method, but often added pitch, resin (resina), turpentine, red lead, and red mercury salts to their own wine for color and "preservation." The three main products of the ancient world had always been, "wine to gladden the heart, olive oil to make his face shine, and bread to strengthen man's heart." (Corn, oil, and wine.)

All Muslims and Arabs hiss and spit at the mention of Hulugu, the Devil Mongol of Genghis Khan's brood, who destroyed Persia, Mesopotamia and her irrigation system, and Syria. Baghdad was obliterated, and the Lebanese towns and cities were scourged by these wine-crazed beasts. Their normal drink had been fermented mare's milk of the Asiatic steppes, but strong wines of the Near East played havoc with the *Yassa,* Genghis Khan's Code of Laws governing strong drink: "A man who is drunk is like one struck on the head. His wisdom and skill availeth him not. Get drunk only four times between full moons or do not get drunk at all. But who amongst warriors can abstain altogether?"

Since man is a genius in discovering stimulants (nearly all peoples have their particular stimulants), fermented alcoholic drinks were discovered very early in the Near East or Fertile Crescent. Ethyl alcohol is a central nervous system depressant, although initial euphoria and feeling of warmth when ingested gave rise long ago to belief in its value as a stimulant. Barley, emmer wheat, and millet were fermented into beers flavored with hops, various spices, bog myrtle, and condiments. Wine was produced from many types of grapes, figs, dates, and Egyptian and Black Sea cherries (the prototype of Cherry Heering®).

Calumell, a Roman botanist born in Cadiz (Gades), Spain, states that grape juice or must had to be boiled so that it would keep until sold. On Cyprus, mustard seeds were first used as a preservative of must, and this practice became general, hence the later English word "mustard." The vessels used in warming the must were made of lead, and poisonous *minium*, or red lead, was added to the wine for color. The cement used to seal storage jars was made of syrup from boiled down must and iris powder in lead or bronze vessels. Hence, wines both good and bad in flavor contained toxic soluble lead salts and other toxic agents. Flavoring like bitter almond (cyanide-rich) and Greek resin caused the drinkers to dilute their wines with water. The shortened lives of many ancient wine bibblers can be explained from this source, i.e. the poisonous additives. Furthermore, fermentations, by various yeasts and torulae and other microorganisms, if not controlled, (as today in these industries) yield not only ethyl alcohol but a number of higher alcohols (amyl and isoamyl), aldehydes, (acrolein or "red eye"), ketones, and acids (all incorrectly called "fusel oil") which are poisonous indeed!

Honey diluted with water was fermented to mead, but this was primarily a barbarian beverage, as was fermented mare's milk. Honey from certain regions and areas was often poisonous. The great Greek physician Claudius Galen (130-200 A.D.,) who was so prominent in the later Roman Empire, always insisted on Attic honey and bread for his dawn meal. Strabo (9.1.23) observed that Attic (Hymettian) honey is the best in the world, especially that gathered from the hives in the region of the ancient silver mines of Attica. This best of all honey is called *acapniston*, because smoke was not employed when the honey was taken from the hives. The flora provided the bees with exceptionally sweet and delicately flavored nontoxic nectars. Naturally, educated men of the Roman-Hellenistic world knew of the classic food-poisoning outbreak from Black Sea honey among the ten thousand of Xenophon, so clearly described in his *Anabasis* of 401 B.C.

After the ten thousand, fleeing from the Persians, reached the Black Sea near Trapesus-Trebizond, "the soldiers camped in some mountain villages which they found well stocked with food and honey and observed a great number of beehives. All of the soldiers who ate of the honey became delirious and suffered vomiting and diarrhea. Those who had eaten a little behaved as though they were drunk, and those who had eaten much of the honey behaved like mad people. Some of these died. Large numbers lay on the ground as though after a defeat and were despondent. Those alive the next day became lucid at about the same hour as they had eaten the honey the day before. On the third and fourth days, they were able to get up. Most of them stated that they felt just as if they had been taking medicine.

It was known later that honey from certain places and regions, was often poisonous, but the mystery remains why the Black Sea Anatolian peoples continued to eat it. Even to this day, the same residents experience this type of poisoning. (Honey poisoning still occurs in New Jersey, Brazil, Asia, Africa, and Asia Minor). Usually, when imported honey is mentioned in Greco-Roman literature, the name of the locality is affixed to it.

The poison is derived from certain nectar-bearing plants: rhododendron, azalea, mountain laurel, palmetto, oleander, and black locust. Modern epidemiologists have now shown that distribution of cases follows closely the distribution of the rhododendron family (Andromeda). The toxin "andromedotoxin" ($C_{31}H_{51}O_{10}$) is heat stable.

Poisonous honey could be added to a variety of foods and beverages since sugar (sakkari from India) was expensive and little used in the Mediterranean world. Fermented solutions of honey (mead), a favorite barbarian drink "in inordinate potations," was, on occasion, known to quell stalwart Nordic warriors who from such ignoble means headed for Valhalla. One of the early sieges of Paris (845 A.D.) by the Danes was "lifted" by this disastrous complaint.

Long millennia before, in prehistoric times in Europe, a dominant people called "Beaker Makers" by the archeologists, anthropologists, and other prehistorians gained ascendency over numerous tribes by use of high-priced beer or ale. They were tall, powerful neolithic racketeers and tended cranially to possess large prominent noses and round heads. The Philistines (Aegean "Pulusati") who conquered in Canaan and who were one of the invading tribes called "Sea People" by the ancient Egyptians, were great barley beer drinkers. Their drinking vessels recovered by archeologists show strainers for the residual barley chaff. The Hebrew accounts in the Old Testament deal harshly with the Philistines with whom the Jews came in contact, like David and Goliath, and Samson and Delilah. Jehovah also inflicted *emerods* on the poor Philistines, both on their front and "hinder ends" (I Sam. 5:6; Ps. 78:66). The prehistoric European Celtic period, known as the La Téne Period, was an inspired culture, "the art of which may largely have owed its existence to Celtic thirst for Greek wine," as Navarro said in 1928. "The Celts (Gauls) would exchange a servant for a drink."

HEMLOCK: THE SOCRATIC POISON

Hemlock is also known as poison parsley, spotted henbane, and in ancient times, as *Conium* fruit. This plant provided one of the better known of the ancient poisons and was used exclusively in the Near East and Mediterranean lands, especially by the Greeks and "Persian Greeks" of Asia Minor, as a judicial poison. It has long been an agent for homicidal and suicidal deaths, Socrates among others having been put to death by drinking its infusions.[68]

The plant *Conium maculatum* is found indigenous to the United States, as well as Europe and Asia. The unripe, but fully grown, fruit contains the principle alkaloid, coniine, and five other toxic alkaloids in lesser amounts. The fatal dose of coniine is 130 mg. We do not know the amount taken by Socrates, but obviously the "kindly jailor" gave him vastly more than needed for lethality. Death occurs in modern cases in a few minutes to three hours.

Symptoms like those recorded during the agonal period of Socrates are a very short period of stimulation, then languor and drowsiness which does not pass into actual sleep. Peripheral nerves become partly paralyzed and the gait, staggering. Speech becomes thick, heart accelerated; respiration is at first accelerated and then irregular until it slows to stoppage. There is no disturbance of the intellect. Also, the sensory apparatus becomes dulled. Death comes as the result of respiratory failure.

The city *(polis)* mobs and their demagogues of the Hellenic and Hellenistic worlds were never kind to philosophers and other intellectuals. Aside from murdering Socrates, called the "noblest man who ever lived," many other good men were "legally" murdered by this poison during these eras. Advantage was taken of the death of Alexander the Great to bring an accusation of impiety against Aristotle. Aristotle quietly left Athens, saying that he would not "give Athens a chance to sin a second time against philosophy." (Grote, Aristotle I. 23). The Athenians passed sentence of death by hemlock upon him but had neither opportunity nor need to execute it. For either through a stomach illness aggravated by his flight, or, as some say, (Diogenes, L., "Aristotle", vii), "by taking poison," Aristotle died a few months after leaving Athens in his sixty-third year of life.

During the rule of the Thirty Tyrants, 404 B.C., a reign of terror began in Athens. The shifty Theramenes, a colleague of Critias, was eventually compelled to drink hemlock.

Nero ordered Seneca to drink hemlock or commit suicide by other means. Resolving to die like Socrates, Seneca drank the infusion and after much suffering, passed away.

Illness and death from *Conium* seeds, roots, and leaves still

---

[68]Imbert-Gourbeyre, A.: *De La Morte de Socrates.* Paris, 1875.

occur. Most of the poisonings from hemlock occur in children who eat the root, thinking it to be parsnips or horseradish. Children also have eaten the leaves with dire results. These varieties of hemlock *(Cicuta)* or "cowbane," but act like *Conium* which also grow in the Eastern states and the Rocky Mountain states, are most frequently observed in Utah. In recent years, most states have established poison centers for differential diagnoses and treatments of both vegetal poisons and chemical preparations.

Migratory quail feeding on hemlock in the Near East have, when eaten by man, caused severe poisoning and death.

In ancient Times writers, such as Theophrastus, Dioscurides, Solinus, and others were not certain about the identification of *Conium* poison, water hemlock and fool's parsley poisons. These toxic preparations were often confused with one another. For instance, Strabo (3.4.18) who was born in Pontus, 64 B.C., and wrote his classic *Geography* in *Circa* 7 B.C., noted that "the Iberians of Spain always keep at hand a poison which is made by them out of an herb that is nearly like parsley and painless, so as to have it in readiness for any untoward eventuality . . . and to die with their liege lord in defeat." This herb perhaps should be identified with the deadly Sardinian herb which Pausanias (10.17) says is like parsley, namely celery-leaved marsh crowfoot (*Ranunculus sceleratus*), and also, according to Dioscurides (*Materia Medica*, 2.206), called by the Hellenes "wild parsley." Solinus wrote that the Sardinian herb produced a convulsive laughter, with a drawing down of the angles of the mouth, and ended fatally with the proverbial "Sardonic smile" on the victim's face which Pausanias described in his classic, *Antiquities of Greece* (second century A.D.).

We list these uncertainties of classification of poisons to illustrate the problems in the history of toxicology. In the sections on *nux-vomica* (containing strychnine) to follow, a better case can be made out for the cause of *risus sardonicus*.

NUX-VOMICA AND CLEOPATRA'S EXPERIMENTS

STRYCHNOS NUX VOMICA is a tree of moderate size native to East Indies, India, and Ceylon. The fruit on the tree is a round berry, as large as an orange, yellow or orange in color, with a hard, fragile rind containing many seeds in a juicy pulp. The seeds contain strychnine and brucine (about 16 per cent alkaloid). The bean of St. Ignatius, also in this genus, contains strychnine as do other species of genus *Strychnos.*

Poisoning symptoms are sudden onset, convulsions, body spasms, body arched backwards and face showing distortion, i.e. *risus sardonicus.* A fatal dose is about ¼ to ½ grain. Death occurs in a few minutes to four hours.

The poison is bitter, and must be masked in food and drink, as has been done in thousands of cases of suicide and homicide.

At Actium before the sea battle with Octavian, Anthony and Cleopatra quarrelled, but two nights later, while at supper, she ordered her cupbearer to fill her cup with the wine all were drinking. After drinking a little of it she offered Anthony her cup as a sign of reconciliation. Greatly moved, Anthony drank from the edge that Cleopatra's lips had touched. She had swiftly dropped in the cup some flowers from the garland on her head. Anthony brought the cup to his lips again, but Cleopatra seized his arm and said, "Do not drink, for the flowers are poisoned." Anthony let his cup drop in terror, and Cleopatra added with passion, "I could have killed you as easily as that, any day, any moment, if only I could live without you."

Back home in her palace in Alexandria, Cleopatra spent some time with her physician, Olympus, who was well versed in the "science of poison," having studied in Assyria the effects of certain plants such as henbane and belladonna, which had the power of causing both death and recovery, according to the dose.[69] Several poisons were prepared by Olympus, and in the presence of Cleopatra were tested on prisoners. Some poisons were quite rapid in action but caused great pain; one was almost instantaneous, but caused convulsions that left the features distorted after death; none seemed to give a prompt and calm death. The fast-acting poison was *nux-vomica* (strychnine) causing the facial distortion *risus sardonicus* described in the previous section. The action of asp venom appeared to satisfy her after observing the deaths of several slaves used as test subjects by Olympus.

In order to escape the Triumph in Rome as the prisoner of Octavian (Caesar Augustus) and the hatred of the citizens of Rome, Cleopatra killed herelf by allowing an asp to bite her, according to all contemporary reports. She was known, however, to carry poison inside a hollow bodkin that she wore in her hair; but it was also known that she kept a deadly small serpent (asp) in a water vessel after Anthony's death. Two puncture wounds resembling snake bite were found on her left arm, not on her breast. The news of the death of this ambitious blond beauty (she was of fair Macedonian ancestry and not brunette) was received with satisfaction in Rome where she had lived as Julius Caesar's mistress and had fomented so much trouble. Hence, the wealth of ancient records about her which we need not pursue further here since Cleopatra's career, fittingly, belongs to Hollywood and George Bernard Shaw.

---

[69]Franzero, Carlo M.: *The Life and Times of Cleopatra.* New York, Philosophical Library, 1957, p. 252-286.

BELLADONNA LEAVES

THIS DEADLY PLANT, (deadly nightshade) is allied to henbane in its specific alkaloids and belongs to the Solanaceae. It is native to Asia Minor, the Fertile Crescent, North Africa, and southern Europe. The poisonous alkaloids—atropine, hyoscyamine, and scopolamine—are found in the leaves in about 0.5 per cent amounts (Merck's Index). The roots contain slightly more than total alkaloids. The berries are also poisonous. The fatal dose is small and not known accurately. The fatal period is a few hours to several days, depending on the dosage.

The extracts of belladonna and henbane were used to poison persons asleep by instilling into the eye or ear. For instance, Burrenich reported that 0.0004 g instilled into the eye of a child caused death (*Ann. Soc. Med. Gand.* 1891 p. 288).

These alkaloid poisons depress the nervous system, and the subject becomes drowsy, finally falling into deep sleep, usually the last. In Hamlet, the poisoner instills poison in the victim's ear.

HENBANE (HYOSCYAMUS)

T HE LEAVES OF THIS plant, *Hyoscyamus niger* of the Solanaceae, when dried, yield .04-.05 per cent of the alkaloids hyoscyamine and scopolamine. The form used by the ancient Egyptians, *H. muticus* contains about 0.5 per cent of the alkaloids. The plant is native to the Fertile Crescent, Africa, and Eurasia. The alkaloid hyoscyamine is extremely poisonous and was used in medicine as a sedative, in 1/240 grain doses.

The genus (eleven species) is sometimes mistaken for parsley, the leaves having a sea-green color, with lethal properties. The lethal dose is small, but not accurately known. It is still used as a suicidal and homicidal agent.[70]

---

[70]Peterson, Haines and Webster, *Legal Medicine,* vol. 2 p. 451, *et. seq.,* 1923; *Merck Index,* 5th ed., 1940; and *U.S. Dispensatory,* any edition.

POISONOUS MUSHROOMS

THE POISONOUS MUSHROOMS of eighty species have long caused illness and fatalities. These vegetal poisons are so well known that little new data can be brought out, except to reiterate that laymen should always eat commercially grown mushrooms. The trained mycologist can eat toadstools of his own choosing. There are five clinical types of mushroom poisoning: (1) gastrointestinal, which is rarely fatal, (2) choleriform, caused by *Amanita phalloides* with about 50 per cent fatalities, (3) nervosus type, with low mortality; (4) sanguinareus (anemia, bloody urine, jaundice), with low mortality rates, and (5) cerebralis (hallucinations, transient excitement), with low fatality, usually recovery. In the first four types, gastrointestinal symptoms are prominent with onset from fifteen minutes to several hours. The chief poison is muscarine (resembles pilocarpine in its action) together with less-known fractions like phallins and glucosides. When dried and powdered, the tissues are very toxic, owing to concentration of poison. Also, when made into an infusion and boiled dry, the residue is extremely poisonous. These soluble powders remain potent for over twenty years, and are quite thermostable.

The most lethal species are A. *phalloides,* or "death cup" and A. *verna,* a subspecies called the "destroying angel." Since fungi have been used as food since recorded history—Babylonians ate them in large quantities as did the Romans—it was learned early that certain species were very toxic indeed. Pliny *(Natural History)* mentions the disastrous results of confusing the various species. Ford[71,72] cites the case of the Greek poet Euripides of Icarus whose wife, daughter, and two sons all died

[71]Ford, W. W.: *Science, 30*:97, 1909.

[72]Ford, W. W.: *Poisonous Mushooms in Legal Medicine and Toxicology.* vol 2. Philadelphia, Peterson, Haines and Webster, 1923. p. 851.

in one day after eating poisonous mushrooms in his absence. One pope and two Roman emperors died from the same cause. Among these men were Clement VII, Jovian, Charles VI, and Claudius.

The poison is extremely toxic, as may be inferred by the case reported by Buttenweiser and Bodenheimer[73] where a seventeen-day-old baby was fatally poisoned from being nursed by its mother who had unknowingly been poisoned that day from eating *A. phalloides!*

Lethal doses for adults are not exactly known, but very small ingested amounts of certain species have caused death. The liver, kidneys, heart, red blood cells, and central nervous system are involved in the toxigenicity.

The ancient, as well as medieval and modern, criminal prepared the lethal extract by boiling the toadstool infusion to dryness, and the concentrated toxins then could be added to food and drink in minute amounts, thus escaping detection. Also, edible and poisonous varieties of mushrooms, when mixed in sauces, meat, and other food preparations, are indistinguishable through the senses. The Latin saying, still useful to mention, runs in translation something like: "If you awaken in the morning after eating wild mushrooms the night before, you know that they were really good mushrooms." Most poisonous varieties taste very good, according to survivors.

We shall cite one example only of mushroom poisoning done with criminal intent in old Rome, although dozens of instances are to be found in the writings of classical authors. Mushrooms were "the poisons of choice."

Emperor Claudius' wife, Agrippina, mother of Nero, reached the throne in power, at least. She had Lollia Paulina put to death, because Claudius, in a careless moment which no wife forgives, remarked on the elegance of Lollia's figure. She had Marcus Silanus poisoned because she feared Claudius might name him his heir. She began a reign of terror in Rome. After five years of this fifth marriage, Claudius awakened to what

---

[73]Buttenweiser, and Bodenheimer: *Deutch. Med. Wschr. 50*:607-608, 1924.

Agrippina was doing. He resolved to put an end to her power and circumvent her plans for Nero by naming Britannicus his heir. But Agrippina had more determination and less scruples. She fed Claudius poisonous mushrooms, and he died after twelve hours without being able to utter a word. When the Senate deified him, Nero, already enthroned, remarked that mushrooms must be the food of the gods, since by eating them Claudius had become a divine dead god, and Nero an Emperor god.[74]

---

[74]Suetonius, "Nero", 52.

CASTOR BEAN POISONS

THE PROPERTIES and uses of the castor bean and its oil had long been known to the ancients, as one must surmise from its use by the ancient Egyptians and Mesopotamians for body-anointing oil and catharsis.

The castor plant was a native of India, but in literate times was cultivated all over the Near East and Mediterranean worlds. Botanically, there were and are now two types and seventeen known varieties. It is circumglobal in cultivation, and occurs as a weed. Much poisoning from the seeds (beans) occur in the new world including the lower Mississippi valley, notably in Oklahoma where it has been studied epidemiologically. In ancient times, as now, the castor oil is pressed out (newer methods involve solvent extraction), and the pressed cake contains the two poisons, ricin, a very toxic protein, and ricinine, an alkaloid ($C_8H_8N_2O_2$) of very toxic properties. This toxic alkaloid is also found in the leaves of the plants *Ricinus communis*. Merck's Index, 5th edition, describes the alkaloid as follows, "Toxic dose 150 mg; small particles in abrasions, eye, or nose may prove fatal. Ricinine accelerates respiration."

The action of the whole bean when swallowed, as it has been by children partaking of wild varieties, is both toxic and allergic in action. Arnold, (Poisoning from castor beans, *Science*, 59:577, 1924) observed the death of a soldier who ate five castor beans for cathartic purposes. Snell, (Hypersensitivity to the castor bean. *Science*, 59:300, 1924), and Robbins, (Poisonous action of the castor bean, *Science*, 58:305-6, 1923) both record severe allergy-like symptoms in castor bean poisoning. There are many references in the literature which point up to lethality of three to five beans when eaten by adults or children. The pressed cake, after oil extraction, is fatal to livestock eating it.

According to Jordan, ricin is an albumin-protein, allied in action to the bacterial toxins. It is a powerful hemolytic agent and is antigenic. Ricin was used in the ancient East for "political purposes." It was added to porridge, bean soup, pea soup, etc., and mixed with masking herbs for criminal purposes.

Benito Mussolini, the defunct dictator of Italy, when in power, employed castor and croton oil in a dastardly way to quell intellectuals who spoke out against him. He would force each person who offended him mightily to ascend a platform in city squares, call together the inhabitants, and have the victim force-fed the oils. Strapped to their rails, the intellectuals were forced by these cathartics to yield to nature in full public gaze and merriment, thus "losing face" from loss of dignity. Catharsis should be a private affair or a "side effect of hospital administration." Mussolini was a cruel man, but numerous older intellectual Italians of Rome whom we interrogated in 1959 recalled these "purges" with laughter! Apparently, they were not the radical intellectual parties who were force-fed the purging agents.

OPIUM AND THE CAVE OF BATS

THE GRAVES OF THE KINGS of Ur in the southern Tigris-Euphrates Valley excavated by the English archaeologist, Sir Leonard Woolley,[75] show the ritual sacrifice of numerous royal servants of many kinds to attend their master's or mistress' business after death. From undisputed evidence of the finds, the victims were unconscious before covered with earth and lying in "good order and alignment." Sir Leonard writes that these victims walked to their places and took the drug opium, which produced deep sleep or death.

Long centuries before these *suttee*-like deaths at Ur, we find that poppies were used in Spain to produce stimulation, sleep, and death.

The Cave of Bats discovered by Don Manuel de Gongora y Martinez[76] a century ago in the Province of Granada presented a startling scene. Holding lanterns high to illuminate the cave, Don Manuel and his companions saw long-dead humans of the Neolithic and Chalcolithic Age dressed in esparto cloth (still used in Spain) lying in a semicircle with their legs and feet turned towards a queen sitting upright against the end wall of the cave, her left hand supporting her chin. The semicircle around her was the bodies of twelve women and three warriors all clothed to the knees with esparto cloth. All the women carried beautiful woven esparto baskets still filled with grain and opium poppy bulbs and seeds—the cause of their quiet deaths. The cave had been sealed thousands of years ago and the cave entrance marked by a Megalithic stone.

In Proverbs (31:6), the compassion for suffering ordered "give strong drink unto him that is ready to perish." In Roman

---

[75]Woolley, L., *Ur of the Chaldees*. Pelican Books, 1950, p. 46-47.

[76]Gongora y Martinez, Manuel de: 1868. *Antiguedades prehistoricas de Andalucia*. Madrid, 1868, pp. 1-58.

133

Judea (mainly at Jerusalem), a society of charitable women provided a merciful drug for those crucified just before nailing to the cross arm. St. Mark cites "wine with myrrh" offered Jesus, but "he received it not." The potion in Palestine, as in the Near East and Greece, is mentioned by Hippocrates in part and in histories of medicine, and was composed of wine and drugs including laudanum (opium), frankincense, myrrh, resin, saffron, and mastich. Laudanum (opium, morphine, etc.) in wine could immobilize and kill in overdoses.

Opium and its derivatives in the hands of the physician have been a boon to suffering mankind. While the opium eaters were at times fanciful poets, the drug in its various forms has caused untold misery, crime, and depravity all through human history.

Forensic scientists have long been occupied with the aftermath of these addictions. "Drugged" wine and foods have been used criminally to stupefy and kill victims for various ends and from various motives. It was one of the "drugs of choice" employed criminally down through the ages.

ACONITE

Aconite was so named from the port of Acone beyond Trapezus on the Black Sea.[77] Aconite is derived from monkshood or wolf's-bane, the dried roots of *Aconitum napellus*. Its habitat is Europe, Asia, and North America, and it contains 0.8 per cent aconitine and 5 other alkaloids. It is very poisonous and is used only in veterinary medicine, if at all, in 1/60 grain doses. It kills man when applied to skin, especially abraded skin. Toxicologists handle aconite with the greatest caution! It is still used in homicide and the fatal dose is 6 mg (0.1 grain).

Death occurs from respiratory failure. Symptoms are numbness, gastrointestinal upset, paralysis of throat, convulsions, and feeble pulse. Aconitine is one of the most powerful natural poisons known, excepting botulinum toxins.

Rome of Juvenal's time,[78] just a century after Horace, was inhabited by a vile population—a nightmare city where "men must dread poison when wine sparkles in a golden cup, and wives learned and proficient in the archpoisoner's arts carry to burial their husband's blackened corpses, and every day in the year you meet a man who has given aconite to a half-dozen relatives."

In *Plutarch's Lives* (Crassus), the use of aconite poison in Parthia (Mesopotamia) is described: "The Parthians who defeated the Romans under Crassus at Carrhae and cut off Crassus' head bore the trophy to their king who was greatly pleased. King Hyrodes, falling into a disease which turned to a dropsy, had aconite given him by his second son Phraates; but the poison working only on the disease, and carrying away the dropsical matter with itself, the king began suddenly to recover, so that

---

[77]Ammianus Marcellinus. Book 12:16, p. 225. Loeb Classical Library, Harvard. Press. Also Strabo (12.3.7).

[78]Juvenal's Satires X, 26; I, 71, 155. Loeb Classical Library, Harvard Press.

135

Phraates at length was forced to take the shortest course and strangled him."

Undoubtedly, Phraates used the crude tuberous root and not the refined alkaloid preparations.

COLCHICINE (COLCHIUM) AND THE
SYRIAN HAMSTER

COLCHIUM IS AND WAS known as the autumn crocus and meadow saffron *(Colchicum autumnale)*. It is indigenous to the eastern Mediterranean basin, especially Syria, where it has grown since the end of the last ice age. The active alkaloid, colchicine, is used by geneticists to effect chromosome doubling, and thus there is a renewed interest in this drug.

The poison resides chiefly in the root and seeds, and the extracts are lethal to adults in 3 to 40 mg doses. As in ancient times, the poison is used today with suicidal and criminal intent—there being some 130 cases on record up to 1930. A usual method of murder was accomplished by placing the seeds in wine, which was done in the celebrated case of Catherine Wilson in 1910 who murdered four persons with the seeds.[79]

Onset of symptoms occur in three to five hours with gastro-intestinal irritation, irregular pulse, and respiratory failure which follows delirium. Since this plant was well known to the ancients, its use as a poison is strongly indicated. During our visit to the Levantine Coastlands, we recorded an observation on colchicine and the Syrian hamster—an animal immune to this poison.

What the Syrians consider minor contributions are the Syrian golden hamsters, so very useful in experimental science, together with the autumn crocus of Syria which proved to contain the alkaloid, colchicine, used to produce chromosome doubling in genetic studies. The elusive hamsters, now so numerous in laboratories of the world, descended from a single pregnant female animal captured in its twenty-foot-deep den near Aleppo in 1920. She delivered twelve kits. Singularly enough, colchicine, or the autumn crocus of Syria, is poisonous to nearly every ani-

---

[79]See Webster, R. W.: *Legal Medicine and Toxicology.* Philadelphia, Saunders, 1930, p. 650.

mal except the Syrian hamster, which indicates selection in this habitat.[80] The hamster was identified as a species in 1839 by the British naturalist, G. R. Waterhouse, at Aleppo, and in 1930, Dr. I. Aharoni captured a litter, as we noted. One male and two female kits were then inbred, and from this progeny came the uncounted hamsters now used in the laboratories of the world. These docile, unique, little rodents with large cheek pouches are so very useful for studies on skin transplants and foreign-tissue grafts (even frog tissues). They provide invaluable experimentation on cancers and are also susceptible to certain viruses. They are most suitable for genetic studies, physiologic studies of hibernation, and immunologic studies. For instance, when human tumors are grafted into its cheek pouches, colchicine given to the animal does not injure the animal but arrests cell division of the tumor, thus providing an unusual method in the fight against cancer.

---

[80]Another instance of inherited defense, as was taught many years ago, is that the white rabbit and other European hares can thrive on a diet of belladonna leaves (atropine or DL-hyoscyamine). Swine are immune to botulinum toxins, ingesting huge doses with impunity but die after eating a few green cockleburrs! Mink are extremely susceptible to Type C botulinum toxin, but other animals are not as sensitive.

THE ASSASSINS AND CANNABIS
INDICA—SATIVA

THE MUSLIMS, like the Christians, broke up into many sects from their quarrels over facets of their religions. The mountainous areas of the Near East provided refuges for these many segregated groups, especially the Lebanon-Antilebanon and Elburz ranges, where numerous sects live to this day.

An interesting sect who inhabited these areas were the Quarmatians, members of a schizmatic and extremely fanatical form of Shiism but related to other groups of Islam. These folk broke up into the Ismailis with their Imams. From this group came another division under Hasan ibn Sabbah who founded the Assassins. He was the original Shaikh-ul-Jabal or "Old Man of the Mountains."

In 1090, this Persian, Hasan al-Sabbah (died 1124 A.D.), broke with the Egyptian Imam and started the new terrible cult in a fortress on an inaccessible spur of the Elburz, 10,200 feet high. He began a campaign of terror when branches sprang up in Syria and Lebanon mountains, strongly fortified in castles still standing. The Order was drawn up much like the later Templars with the "Old Man of the Mountains" as commander of grand masters, grand priors of districts, and "self sacrificers," the working Assassins. The "workers" or Assassins (Arabic = hashish drug) would "swallow" the potent Asian drug and set out on their missions, killing designated persons of high and low position. Richard the Lionhearted was spared by them because the assassin masters hated Saladin. Marco Polo described their activities in detail. The initiates were promised Paradise, win, lose, or draw.

The fiery Mamaluke Baybars destroyed the Syrian group and the Mongols exterminated the Elburz assassins, but fleeing remnants known as Ismailites are now found in North Syria (Alawites), Persia, Oman, Zanzibar, and India. Aga Khan of

Bombay was the leader of that group but lived in Europe. Of course, they do not practice the Assassin-cult now. The French military (1919-1924) in the Near East, holding mandated Syria by force, informed the international press that the cult was not extinct so far as "Saltwater Franks" were concerned! Local Christians, mostly Maronites, were called "Freshwater Franks."

The Assassins (ultra-Shiites) and Crusaders built similar mountain castles and the Hospitallers were always allies of the Assassins. When the Crusaders entered Syria from the northwest, the Assassins were entering from the northeast where both groups acquired strongholds. The Assassin Grand Master of Syria controlled 60,000 men. He, Rashid-al-Din Sinan, had numerous Christians and Muslims murdered, among them Raymond II of Tripoli, Conrad de Montferrat who was King of Jerusalem, and others of note. Failing to murder Saladin in two attempts, the orthodox Muslims moved against Sinan and punished him with sanctions. St. Louis IX, the cannonized King of France, when at Acre, exchanged gifts with the chief Assassin. It is now known that the Hospitallers and Templars copied the table of organization of the Assassins, i.e., a grand master, priors, propagandists, and devotees who made assassination a fine art, as well as practiced the most villainous dissimulation. Just as the great Baybars destroyed their strongholds and power, the Roman Church eventually destroyed or "nullified" the Hospitallers and Templars.

When the Crusaders were pitted against Saladin (Salahuddin-al-Ayyubi, 1169-1192 A.D.), who was a blond Kurd, they met their match and more. He was a Sunni orthodox Muslim and loved Islam. He was connected with Baalbec in Lebanon, where his father was a commander of the military. The Christians made a deal with the Assassins to kill Saladin, the noblest man of the Crusaders' wars and called today in the West "the best Christian of them all!" A large sum was paid, but the killers failed. Muslims were irate that the Neo-Ismaili Order should also kill Muslims. The "Old Man of the Mountains" was taken but paroled when he vowed never again to raise his hand against Saladin. He kept his promise.

Ibn Battuta (born 1305 A.D.), the greatest land explorer of all time, travelled deep into the African desert and jungle, Arabia, Inner Asia, Spain, Italy, India, Ceylon (Serandib), Anatolia, Indonesia, Malay Penninsula, and China. His descriptions from Canton to Timbuktu, geographic and ethnologic, remain unsurpassed. He told much of Gaza, Hebron, Jerusalem, Acre, Tyre, Tripoli, Kerak, Antioch, and Damascus. He described the Assassins of the Syrian branch "who are the arrows of the Sultan who strikes his enemies who live or escape to other lands."

When Hulugu and his Mongols and Asian Christian allies devastated the Near East in 1226, many of the surviving Assassins who had this "scourge of Allah" in mind were hunted down and tortured to death. The escapees scurried away to all points of the compass.

Some of the Assassins survived both Crusaders, Mongols, and Saracens. Their descendents, the Ismailis, inhabit their old mountain fastness. Their sect has large followings in India, East Africa, Sudan and Egypt who venerate the Aga Khan of India. They know him as Mohamed Shah. His picture hangs prominently in the houses of every family of the sect.

The drugs from Indian hemp or *C. indica* (Americans call it marihuana) now found to be in the tissues of a plant with varieties of almost world-wide habitat, was the hashish of the Hashishans or Assassins which the Old Man of the Elburz Mountains provided for his "arrows" or assassins. He also provided a beautiful *paradise* or garden, well-supplied with beautiful maidens and every sensual want as an adjunct and adjuvant to his new religion and rituals. He was never in want of converts! With these inducements and drug effects, "illusions of heaven and abode of their souls" the Old Man and his successors insured salvation with the key of heaven for his usually successful murderers. The terror of his power was great among Muslim sects, Christians both local and European Crusaders, Byzantines, Jews and Mongols.

The drug obtained from the dried flowering top of the pistillate *C. sativa* and *C. indica,* is a mixture of cannabine, cannabinol, muscarine, trigonelline, with cannabinol the most active principle. Hypnotic effects, stimulation, and "demonic roseate concepts" leading to acts of violence are still the effects of this terrible habit-forming drug when swallowed without resorting to the rituals provided by the "Old Man of the Mountains." The preparations were ingested and obviously not smoked in "reefers" or "pot" as is done today by "juveniles of all ages." Users of *C. sativa,* a much less potent American variety, when using the stronger Far East *C. indica,* may react in much the same manner as did the Assassins of old. Some Mexican varieties are unusually potent. Smoking was long practiced by Asians (hemp, opium), and by their remote kinsmen, the Amerinds (tobacco mixtures). Hemp (*C. indica*) smoking equipment and perfectly preserved frozen bodies were found recently by Russian archaeologists in the frozen tombs of Western (Scythian) Siberia, dated *Circa* 500 B.C., thus confirming Herodotus (484-425 B.C.) Book IV, who described them in detail as well as their uses of hemp for smoke, rope, and textiles.

NICOTINE, THE FIRST CIGARETTE, AND SHAH ABBAS

NICOTINE IS THE CHIEF constituent of tobacco *(Nicotiana tabacum)* which presents toxicologic interest aside from cardiac and general toxicity and the carcinogenic potentials of smoke constituents. The alkaloid is found throughout the plant but especially in the leaves, which contain from 0.6% to 8.0% depending upon the kind of tobacco. Crude nicotine preparations have been used as insecticides. There are many records of fatal cases of poisoning from nicotine, but medical interest remains with smokers and chewers, who with some frequency present symptoms of gastrointestinal irritation and illness aside from cardiac and circulatory disturbances and lung cancer. These are, of course, isolated cases or incidents and these can be differentiated from food-borne illness (see "Lead Poisoning" from lead arsenate).

We shall include a historical note on cigarettes and tobacco smoking, which we wrote while in the Near East (Lebanon and Syria).

The gifts of the noble red men of the New World to the Old World are many and varied in usage. Their contributions to world betterment are all-too-briefly listed: corn (maize), potatoes, tomatoes, chocolate, vanilla, peanuts, pineapples, and scores of other useful foods, drugs, and devices and substances, including rubber. Tobacco and corn (maize) spread rapidly over the Near and Far East. In 1574, the great German botanist, Leonhard Rauwolf, found the lands of the Euphrates covered with waving fields of New World corn. One gift of dubious value from the Caribbean Indians to the peoples of our planet was syphilis, but the poor Indians received smallpox, several different venereal diseases, and a host of infectious diseases in return, contracted under more austere conditions.

Tobacco, like syphilis and maize, diffused rapidly after 1493, but not without frowns of officials of the "seventy nations of mankind" as the Septuagint of ancient Alexandria would have it.

The Persians and Syrians early learned to filter tobacco smoke through water to "purge it of all the oily and gross qualities of tobacco." Many people used tobacco in excess, and the devout Shah Abbas, who despised the habit, devised a trick for his courtiers. Substituting dried horse manure for tobacco, he invited his noblemen to "smoke a costly tobacco from the Vizier of Aleppo." The nobles puffed away, extolling it to the skies in their rich Arabian language, calling this batch "the aroma of a thousand flowers." "Damn the drug of tobacco," cried the Shah, "which cannot be distinguished from horse dung!"

Laurence Oliphant, an eccentric person, who travelled and lived in the Near East with the Turks, returned to England after the Crimean War. He introduced the cigarette into London drawing rooms. It had been invented thirty years before by a Lebanese-Syrian gunner of the Acre garrison. This resourceful Muslim, finding that the quartermaster had sent them tobacco but no pipes to smoke it in, hit upon the bright idea of wrapping the tobacco in rolled up nitrate-impregnated fusepaper. It smoked evenly, and the idea was so appreciated that during the Crimean War, the treated, paper-covered cigarettes made their appearance in the British army. So many British soldiers lost their pipes during the "charges" and encampments that they took to rolling their tobacco in paper like the Turks. And so the cigarette is supposed to have been popularized.

The Mexican Indians had been rolling their own with corn husks (cigarito) and tough tobacco leaves before Columbus, a custom which the Spanish colonists adopted at once (cigars, cigarellos). The Syrians and Lebanese treat their tobacco leaves by curing with fragrant smokes, and for home use, mixing it with dried leaves such as grape leaves. The curing of tobacco in the Levant, Turkey, Egypt, and Greece entails some half-secret processes. The Syrians employ a green wood smudge from an aromatic shrub impregnating the tobacco leaves during the curing process.

All of this business led the medics of the world, with statistical help, to argue about lung cancer and filter tips. Many American cigarettes are of a "Turkish" blend which can mean the different aromas of Latakia, or other Syrian blends, as well as those of Smyrna (Izmer), Greek, Egyptian, Iraqi, and Persian origins. They are all better than Shah Abbas' *ersatz,* which civilians asserted they were sold during World War II. Some prejudice has long existed against cigarette smoking, and this reaction has lately accelerated from statistical data reflecting impairment of health from this cause. The popular evangelist, Billy Sunday, in the early twentieth century summed up the cigarette situation by his remark: "A fire on one end and a fool on the other."

CARBON MONOXIDE (CO)

INHALATION OF POISONOUS gases such as sulfur dioxide, hydrogen sulfide, hydrogen cyanide, marsh gas of mines, smelter fumes, and escaping refrigeration gases, all have caused grave illnesses and death. Both Sir Charles Sherrington[81] and Dr. Yandell Harrison observed that carbon monoxide has caused more deaths and illness than all other gases: "Carbon monoxide is the prime enemy of all red-blooded creatures," uniting as it does with both hemoglobin and myoglobin of the muscles and thus preventing oxygenation of tissues.

Since carbon monoxide unites and binds with most body pigments, the carbon monoxide content of auto exhaust and cigarette smoke can impair vision and the heart. The walls of blood vessels, when exposed to carbon monoxide become more permeable and thus aid in deposition of lipids (cholesterol, fats) to the walls which can eventually clog the arteries.

In the changeover to right-hand traffic in Stockholm (1967), during the thirty-hour ban on private traffic, the conservationist, Hans Palmstierna, found the atmospheric carbon monoxide curve at street level to have been reduced to nondetectable amounts. In New York City, the carbon monoxide content of the air of a busy, heavy-traffic street averages 10 to 15 ppm; lead = 8 μg/ cu m. An unexpected source of carbon monoxide is the upper layers of water of the continental shelf which contributes to the atmosphere about 5.5 per cent of the amount emitted by burning of fossil fuels! The source was at one time thought to be due to pollution and indirectly to biologic action of marine life. The origin or origins are not yet known.

Many epidemiologists became interested in carbon monoxide poisoning, largely because this entity was so often confused

---

[81]Sherrington, Sir Charles. *Man on His Nature*. New York, Cambridge University Press, 1951, p. 82.

with bacterial food poisoning.[82] As an example, an outbreak arising from faulty gas connections and adjustment of gas burners by the householder was diagnosed locally by the attending physician and subsequent hospital records as food poisoning of bacterial origin caused by eating canned pork and beans and meat. The symptoms common to three of five who suffered illness (onset of which spread over twenty-four hours) were nausea, vomiting, diarrhea, headache, malaise, dimness of vision, and cyanosis. Careful investigations (meeting reticence as usual) showed (1) the gas leaks and rooms with highest concentrations, (2) the failure to notify the gas company when moving into the dwelling, (3) faulty differential diagnosis, (4) two people who were "cyanotic" only and (5) dreams of sudden riches (don't we all?). The cases came to trial in a Federal Court on the theory of implied warranty resulting in a directed verdict for the two defendant companies. This verdict was upset by the appellate court, and the case was reset for trial. After a lengthy hot fight the second jury found for the defendants. Plotkin and Kapplow[83] have called attention to the difficulties that may arise when carbon monoxide poisoning is mistaken for food poisoning.

Three additional outbreaks of this nature involving, in all, twenty people were investigated by us, but the parallel nature of the legal pictures preclude need for further mention except to consider the symptoms, dosage, sequelae, and history of this noxious agent.

The symptoms depend largely on concentration of carbon monoxide gas. In case of large doses, the patient becomes unconscious with death resulting from respiratory and cardiac failure. One part of carbon monoxide in one hundred parts of air when breathed only for a few minutes will cause death. In smaller doses not actually measured, headache, throbbing temples, dimness of vision and gastrointestinal symptoms ensue (diarrhea,

---

[82] Jensen, L. B.: Food Poisoning. *J. Forensic Sci.*, 2:355-372, 1957.

[83] Plotkin, S., and Kapplow, R.: Food poisoning and carbon monoxide poisoning. *N. Y. State J. Med.*, 52:2409-2411, 1952.

vomiting, nausea). The pulse is fast, as is respiration. Cyanosis of lips is often noticeable. Grave sequelae are recorded, such as loss of memory, multiple neuritis, temporary blindness, muscle pains, recurring headaches, and weakness.[84] After the Battle of Jutland, many German navy personnel entering Kiel and "exercising and drinking" on leave fell dead from shell cordite monoxide aftereffects. Rest is essential for recovery. Mental deterioration often follows carbon monoxide poisoning. Jensen[85] examined a thirty-four-year-old male who had attempted suicide with this gas. At intervals of two years and nine years after gassing, the patient's mental ability remained at a fourteen-year-old level.

Ever after man's first success in using fire, some hazards of carbon monoxide poisoning have existed. Today, combustion of our fossil fuels remains a grave threat to our respiratory pigments and enzymes of the metabolic cycles and pathways. Building engineers and engineers in the broad field of combustion are increasingly concerned with the problem.

Vitruvius (*circa* 1 A.D.), the great Roman engineer and architect, wrote, "The immense size of Rome makes it needful to have a vast number of habitations, and as the ground platt is small and not sufficient to have one-story habitations for the multitude, the nature of the case compels us to have highrise buildings." There were, shortly after the time of Christ, some 44,000 tenement blocks *(insulae)* in Rome and about 1800 separate mansions *(domus)*, housing a population between 1,500,000 and 1,700,000. Juvenal and others describe these "vermin-infested sleeping pockets upon the fifth and sixth floors" as "slightly better than rooms on the lower floors." In Tyre, Sidon, and Arvad of Lebanon at this time, Strabo tells us these tall *insulae* were built up to eight floors, but at Rome the city engineers persuaded the rulers to limit *insulae* to no more than

---

84See Wilson and Winkleman: Multiple neuritis following carbon monoxide poisoning. *J.A.M.A., 82*:1408, 1924.

85Jensen, M. B.: Mental deterioration following carbon monoxide poisoning. *J. Abnorm. Psychol. 45*:146-153, 1950.

four or five floors because of lack of water pressure from the aqueducts and hazards of demolition from faulty construction and fire (Rich Romans like the noble Cicero and ignoble Crassus invested in these "rabbit warrens"). They were usually windowless with poor ventilation, except for wooden shutters which were closed at night from fear of bad night air (*mal aria, i.e. malaria*). The Romans of Italy and the Imperial City heated their rooms with portable charcoal-burning braziers. There was "suffocation" reported as a usual event, and suicides were known to occur by sealing a room, thus proving that the Romans knew of the poisonous nature of the "fumes" or gas.[86]

In *Plutarch's Lives*, "Cassius Marius," the death of Catalus Lutatius, Marius' colleague in Consulship and in the Triumph over the Jutland Cimbrians is ascribed to "suffocation." Catalus, when proscribed by Marius, shut himself up in a sealed room and burned a large "fire of charcoal." This was a carbon monoxide death, with oxygen depletion as an adjuvant factor.

Gaseous poisonings in the ancient world also resulted from fires in lime kilns, brick and pottery kilns, charcoal kilns, iron ore works, and nonferrous metal smelters called "tarshish" in northwest Semite records from Spain through Syria-Palestine to Asia Minor. (Tarsus of St. Paul, Tarshish of Aqaba, Tartetos of Cadiz and so on).

Today, after thorough laboratory researches showing the avidity of carbon monoxide for hemoglobin, myoglobin, and the many enzyme systems including ferratin, one becomes increasingly apprehensive about the sequelae of this dreadful poison omnipresent in our environments. Carbon monoxide combines with hemoglobin and myoglobin some three hundred times more readily than does oxygen to form the carboxy compounds which cannot transport or accept oxygen. Moreover, the carboxy compounds in the living animal and *in vitro* impair the functions of the normal pigments. Hence, the gassed organism undergoes "internal strangulation." The carboxy compounds, in the presence of pure oxygen, do give up carbon monoxide after a time, but

---

[86]Haskell, H. J.: *Cicero.* New York, 1942, p. 379.

the surviving victim often suffers irreparable damage, usually as described above in this section.

BROKEN GLASS AND POWDERED
DIAMOND IN FOOD AND DRINK

PHYSICIANS, SURGEONS, and investigators have long been interested (or irked?) when confronted with the problem of people of all ages (one to ninety) who have had foreign substances such as chicken bones, fish bones, fruit stones and pits, needles and pins of all sorts, coins, and so on lodged in their buccal cavity, esophagus, windpipes, stomach and intestines (at any point along the "thirty feet from mouth to terminus"). These are trying ordeals for all concerned. The great anxiety of patients who have swallowed broken glass from glassware, bottles, and thermos bottles while drinking, or glass bits in foods of all sorts is melancholy to behold.

Food and beverage manufacturers are often beset with claims for damages arising from persons alleged to have eaten foods or drunk beverages containing glass particles prepared by financially solvent companies. The usual claimant is a "glass case," but many other foreign substances are in the picture. We compiled a list of 124 substances alleged to have been foreign to the foods which we examined during the past forty years. Among these were a rubber hot dog, an upper right molar tooth (3rd), a Roosevelt dime, a "Crow for Cox" campaign button, a rubber contraceptive, one green frog, many aerial insects and spiders, a shoe horn and a cherry pit in a cherry pie!

The layman has always been frightened of swallowing splintered or powdered glass. During World War I, German agents in Britain and America were rumored to have added powdered glass to foods like cheese, sausage, and breads. The panic was allayed first by the British Ministry of Health who found splintered and powdered glass to be harmless when swallowed (Hancock, G. C.: *Ministry of Health Reports on Public Health*, No. 37, London). The Germans were innocent of this type of "warfare."

Simmons and von Glahn (*J. A. M. A., 71*:2127, 1918) fed ground glass to dogs with no evil effects. The authorities, Jordan and Tanner, found that the danger in glass particles in foods is practically *nil*. Dr. Exner (*Arch. Physiol. 89*:253) observed that a glass fragment in the intestines is rejected by the mucosa, and if a splinter of glass (lead glass is opaque to X-rays) is observed in passage, the long axis of the splinter is aligned with the long axis of the lumen of the gut and by normal motility of the intestines is gently pushed along to evacuation.[87]

There are instances, however, when swallowed glass fragments appear to have caused grave damage with hemorrhage in the intestinal tract. The whole picture can be found in the more extensive handbooks on legal medicine and toxicology.

Like almost everyone with whom we have talked about the glass problem, we also have swallowed some gritty powdered glass in food and drink without experiencing any untoward effects. We never volunteered to swallow broken glass, but two professors of physiology (Emory and Virginia Universities) were employed by beverage and food companies in trials of cases to "eat" glass fragments from corresponding glass alleged to have been swallowed by the plaintiffs in the cases (1927 to 1940). The professor would have the bottle or glass container broken in the courtroom when called to testify, and after taking the oath, i.e. "being sworn." Then, after testifying and enduring cross-examination, he would swallow five pieces of the approximate size and shape alleged to have entered the claimant's department of the interior. The jurors would watch this procedure goggle-eyed. The witness then sat in a chair in full view of the jury during the remaining time of the trial and longer if called upon to do so. The jurors were deaf to the rest of the trial and watched the professor closely with suspicion of magic tricks and also with anxiety for the reckless man. No harm resulted to these two witnesses, but we observed that they very carefully counted the glass fragments after defecation!

---

[87]Jensen, L. B.: *Microbiology of Meats,* 3rd ed. Champaign, Garrard Press, 1954, p. 406.

We recall another incident where a husband and wife motoring over the California desert drank some orange juice from their thermos jar. The wife noticed some grits after swallowing the juice and the husband gulped a larger drink when he spat out glass. The thermos glass had broken! The nearest physician was two hundred miles away. Upon reaching the doctor's village, they learned that he was away some hundred miles on a case. By that time, the husband, finding his wife and himself without symptoms or hurt (except fright) in any way, decided that glass was not so very dangerous and drove back to Orange County. Next morning, he called his family physician who prescribed some bulking colloid and intestinal antiseptics with the order to examine the feces for blood and glass. There was glass found and a few specks of bright red blood from the anal orifice. There were no sequelae except the materials for a good story—often told.

A case for damages from allegedly eating a hot dog with glass in it came up up just one year after the accident in a county court in the Connecticut valley. The woman plaintiff testified that she ate two frankfurters, butterless bread, and black coffee on Thanksgiving day (Roosevelt's Thanksgiving Day— earlier than the conventional date). The half of the second frank as exhibit "A," then a year old, contained a piece of shattered old window pane. The meat was slightly rancid, but firm, reddish, and recent in origin. A year's storage of the frank in the refrigerator, as testimony indicated, would have resulted in wrinkling and drying to a hard, slender, wrinkled piece. The plaintiff's lawyer was a cross "cross-examiner" and belted us with sarcasm and insult (permitted by the elected judge). Passing the exhibit to the eight lady jurors (the four male jurors were not "bushy tailed" this day) each juror then inspected the frank containing the piece of glass and showed disgust for the whole business, including the court. They remained out just two minutes and returned an unanimous verdict for the defendants. We were chided by the other side and the court because we could not estimate the age of the glass as closely as we testified to the age of the "doctored" hot dog of recent ancestry! The Corning Museum of Glass and Corning Laboratories have developed methods revealing age and nature of glasses from antiquity and subsequent times, but Corning's vast knowledge of this subject was not needed in this trial. (Corning publishes a journal covering all aspects of glass from prehistoric and historic archeologic sites.)

Cellini (1500-1571 A.D.), the famous sculptor and goldsmith[88] had been thrown into a Roman dungeon by Paul and Pier Luigi but at last was permitted to have a larger room. At their instigation, according to Cellini, a slow poison was to be placed in the food given him. The ancient "slow poison" was to produce its usual effect in four to five months. This was the then well-known powdered diamond preparation in which each small particle has sharp cutting edges that penetrate the mucosa of the intestines and kill eventually with hemorrhage, peritonitis, and colitis.

Fortunately, says Cellini, the goldsmith entrusted with the task of powdering the diamond of the conspirators was avaricious and poor, so he substituted a beryl of little value. Cellini ate heartily of the "salad, sauce, and pottage" and felt the victuals "scrunch between my teeth. . . . When I finished, I saw some fine and glittering particles on the remnants on the plates" . . . Collecting them . . . I gave myself up without doubt as dead . . . had recourse with pious heart to holy prayers."

Then, becoming calmer, he took some particles on his knife and crushed them on the prison bars where they yielded and crumbled. Needless to say, Cellini was greatly relieved because it had long been common knowledge that powdered glass, gems other than diamond, or other stones and ceramic materials were harmless when ingested.

Thereafter he would not eat anything given him, but secretly ate bread provided by a fellow prisoner, the Bishop of Pavia. Eventually, the Cardinal of Ferrara, by a stratagem, got Cellini released "in the nick of time."

---

[88]*Autobiography of Benvenuto Cellini* (Symonds Translation), New York, Liverwright, p. 295 ff., 1942.

Cellini's own idea (a modern one also, as said to be shown in dog experiments) of the action of powdered diamond was as follows. "Now the diamond is not a poison, but its incomparable hardness enables it, unlike ordinary stones, to retain very acute angles, when every other stone is pounded, that extreme sharpness of edge is lost; their fragments becoming blunt and rounded. The diamond stone preserves its trenchant qualities; wherefore, if it chances to enter the stomach together with food, the peristaltic motion needful to digestion brings it into contact with the coats of the stomach and bowels where it sticks, and by the action of fresh food forcing it further inwards, after some time perforates the organs. This eventually causes death. . . ."

Postmortem examination of dogs fed small diamond particles are purported to show that the particles, unlike glass or stone fragments, have a chemotaxis for the mucosa and penetrate the gut in one to four months, causing diarrhea, inflammation, and finally peritonitis. Thus it could be perhaps one of the "slow poisons" of ancient and medieval times.

The mineral diamond was a prized stone in the Orient, Fertile Crescent, and the Greco-Roman world. Perfect faceting in those times was, of course, accidental. St. Augustine of Hippo (354-430 A.D.) of later Roman times writes of it: "The diamond is a stone possessed by many, and the stone is so hard that it can be wrought neither by iron or by fire, nor, they say, by anything at all except goat's blood. . . . Persons who have not seen it perhaps do not believe what is said of it, or if they do, they wonder as at a thing beyond their experience. . . ." (*The City of God*. New York, The Modern Library, p. 768). Cleopatra is known to have possessed diamonds from India. Powdered or crushed diamonds were supposedly added to foods and as "lees" in wines in antiquity for lethal purposes, according to inferences, not precise statements, from surviving manuscripts.

The question of ground diamond—dust and fragments—as a slow-acting lethal agent has been debated in modern forensic-science circles for a long time. Kunz[89] mentions the pros and

[89]Kunz, G. F.: *The Curious Lore of Precious Stones*. New York, Halcyon House, 1938, pp. 152-157.

cons of the subject, citing pseudo-Aristotle, Avicenna, Garcias ab Orta (in India), and others who held firmly to the view that diamond fragments would rupture the bowel with fatal results. Turkish Sultan Bajaset II died from a dose of powdered diamond administered to him by his son, Selim, who mixed the dust with the Sultan's food (Pindar: *De adamenti*. Berolini, 1829, p. 58). The disciples of Paracelsus alleged that he was murdered in the prime of life by a dose of diamond dust, although this was disputed by Ambrosius (Aldrovandi: *Museum Metallicum*. Bononiae, 1648, p. 949).

At age forty-four, Lorenzo, "the Magnifico," de Medici was about burned out with living, i.e. domestic discord, finance, and women. Sinister omens heralded his death, such as a terrific hurricane and his zoo animals which fought to the death. He lay in torment with severe stomach pains. His physician, Pier Leonti of Spoleto, treated him with the medicine of the times and then gave him a beverage containing powdered diamond, speeding "the Magnifico" on his way. This merciless potion also doomed Pier Leonti with his great patient, for the physician was found dead at the bottom of a well the day after Lorenzo died.[90]

The Countess of Essex employed one James Franklin, an apothecary, in 1613, to kill Sir Thomas Overbury by administering powdered diamond to him. Overbury lingered three months and then she gave him, while he was imprisoned in the Tower of London, a dose of corrosive sublimate ($HgCl_2$) which ended poor Overbury's suffering.[91]

Tycho Brahe, the famous Danish astronomer, at the age of fifty-five years, died in Prague, October 13, 1601, greatly honored by his contemporaries—especially by Kepler, his student who correctly said that "Tycho's observations had led to a complete revolution of astronomy." A stubborn discrepency of 8 arc minutes between Tycho's observations (without telescope) of the longitude of Mars and the established circular epicycles of long

[90]Lucas-Dubreton, J.: *Daily Life in Florence in the Time of the Medici*. New York, Macmillan, 1961.

[91]Amos: *The Great Oyer of Poisoning*. London, 1846, p. 336.

standing resulted in a saying: "Tycho gave Kepler the place to stand on, and Kepler moved the world!" On that October evening, Tycho was invited to supper at the house of the Baron of Rosenberg, along with the Imperial Councillor, Ernfried Minkawitz. During the supper, he was seized with acute illness. He suffered for ten days with fever, abdominal pains, and delirium. When the morning of October 24 came, the delirium left him, and feeling the approach of death, he called for his family, pupils, and friends. He died exhausted but lucid and was entombed in the Teynkirche (Tynskykostel) of Prague where the body still rests. A rumor soon spread that Tycho Brahe had died of poison administered by envious courtiers or by his archenemy, Reymers Bär. As the latter died fourteen months before his supposed victim, it would have been a remarkably slow poison. Numerous speculations have been made since that day, but none proved to be a satisfactory explanation. Some of the conjectured poisons, at one time or another, were listed as arsenic, antimony, vegetal and alkaloidal poisons, and, of course, diamond dust, the "slow poison." Tycho usually added antimony to his own formula for theriaca!

Dr. Kunz still maintains that powdered diamond is not injurious, but presumably neither he nor any toxicologist would volunteer to swallow a dose to prove their point. There are other present-day toxicologists who doubt the injurious effects of diamond fragments in the intestinal tract. We have inquired about the dangers, if any, from diamond cutters who are most precise and careful technologists. Their answers were equivocal. A few of these good men took pains to avoid diamond dust and unexpected tiny fragments so far as danger of ingestion went and regard their work as hazardous only when cleavage of planes resulted in a "smash" with great monetary loss. Any human volunteers to settle this question?

ARSENIC AND THE MURDER
OF NAPOLEON

Poisoning with criminal intent by means of arsenical compounds was long an established routine of murder. Today, this method is not often encountered in this country but elsewhere does go on according to the literature and notices in the daily press.

We shall outline a few outbreaks and cases which we encountered and investigated with others, including insurance company investigators. A woman of childbearing age had "lost" two husbands—heavily insured—and two insured children. An insurance investigator, noting the collection claims for the last dead and buried husband, compared notes with the other insurers and started the slow-moving legal machinery for exhumation which was finally ordered for the four graves. Both our laboratory and the coroner's chemist found large amounts of arsenic (oxides) in the gastrointestinal tracts and tissues of the embalmed bodies. The woman retained a then well-known criminal lawyer and much artful dodging went on before the trial of the case. The defendant alleged that she had contracted syphilis at a former period in her life and was confused about the disease until the demise of her last husband. According to her testimony and that of a peculiar physician employed by her counsel, she "undoubtedly passed the disease to those dead in her family because they, in turn, all underwent neo-Salvarsan® arsenical treatments." This would account for the arsenic found by the state and in our Chicago laboratory (clinical and analytical). The jurors carefully chosen by the "master lifesaving attorney for the defendants" (as best he could and he was good at this phase of "courtin'"), and those chosen by the State listened attentively and seemed pleased at this turn in the case. The State countered with the large amounts of soluble arsenic found in all four exhumed bodies which apparently demolished the contentions of the other side. The "adroit" (to misuse a word) defense lawyer then recalled his physician to the witness stand, who thereupon testified that the arsenic found by the State entered the bodies through the embalming fluid! The State countered with the fact that soluble arsenic or arsenic in any form was not used in these fluids. After a huddle of lawyers in the judge's chamber, it was stipulated that a referee chemist be appointed and directed to one well-known funeral home designated (by the other side) to obtain a sample of fluid for analysis by both sides in the case. The State's attorney and insurance lawyers were trusting souls! The fluid contained arsenic! The jury found for the woman, the insurers lost, and that was that. Not long afterwards we talked with this criminal lawyer who (being immune now in Chicago since the case was closed) told us of his daring night entry into the designated embalmer's room. With the help of a lockpicker—a former client—he entered this establishment with a pound of arsenic trioxide, dumped it into the fluid and mixed it as well as he could. The embalmer was, of course, innocent of the whole matter but was understandingly greatly "perplexed and irritated."

The most remarkable ancient lawsuit of record was that in which Cicero (66 B.C.) prosecuted Oppianicus in a very complex, lurid, poisoning case. Cicero's record of this trial is to be found in his *Pro Cluentio* which was brought to mind by the foregoing poisoning case. Modern and ancient motives which lead to criminal poisonings are not unlike, and the legal dodges, spirit of contentions, infighting of families, and eventual clarification of the issues are all stated classically by Cicero, Rome's greatest orator and lawyer of the era.

At this time, we find it pleasant to state that defendant lawyers engaged largely in civil court practices are, by-and-large, the most gentlemanly ethical men of any profession that we were privileged to meet. As a scientist, we recall all of them with admiration and respect. Within a year's time, they individually had been engineers, physician-surgeons, traffic experts, microbiologists, toxicologists, corporate-law experts, marine-law experts, and a long list of other specializations. A few of them with whom we worked revealed astonishing acumen and were knowledgeable in integrating data and simplifying facts for understanding by court and jury.

Another case in which we did not participate occurred in 1914 in Chicago. During a banquet at a hotel for Archibishop M., where 250 people sat at table, an acute illness was suffered by all in about ten minutes to an hour after partaking of the soup served to them. Fortunately none died, but all were acutely ill with the composite symptoms of vomiting, severe colic, vertigo, headache, muscle spasms, and other effects of arsenic poisoning. Analysis of the soup revealed 1.3 grams of arsenic trioxide per quart. An anti-Catholic male cook disappeared from the hotel kitchen just before the soup was served and was never apprehended.

Another outbreak of arsenical poisoning in a poverty-stricken country family, which we first became aware of when suit was filed for damages from alleged food poisoning from cotton oil shortening, precluded on-the-spot-investigation, but the plaintiff's counsel preserved the identifiable shortening in all good faith. This lawyer had been an elected state representative and was a thoroughly honest man with hard-hitting courtroom tactics. The shortening was, upon chemical and spectrographic analysis and standard laboratory animal-feeding tests, found to be devoid of poisons including arsenic. It was finally admitted by one of the children (a motherless family of father and five children tended by the nine-year-old eldest daughter) that a "bag of arsenic for the potatoes and garden" was suspended from the cabin ceiling by a string out of reach as was the custom in that area of our country. None in this pathetic family died, but all vomited after eating "fried cakes" and were stricken for weeks. Under cross-examination during the third trial of this case, the nine-year-old girl broke down and fearfully admitted that she had somehow gotten the white arsenic confused with white flour in making the dough. There was certainly no criminal intent here! The first trial of these cases ended in a nonsuit, the second trial ended in a "hung jury," and the last trial, in which the evidence and arguments went to the jury of sleepy farmers at midnight, resulted in a quick finding for the defendant companies. The closing arguments of the other side were directed largely at the testimony of the present writer. Seeing that the evidence was hardly in his favor, this lawyer exhorted the jury and turned his accusative dexter finger at me. I was sitting with the spectators. "Gentlemen of the jury," he intoned, "look at sly old Doc Jensen sitting there. He fed the shortenin' to poor defenseless guinea-pigs. . . . Did he eat any of it himself? . . . No siree! Not astute, sly old Doc. He is too smart to do that. It is for you to weigh why he did not eat it." Even the most dour juror grinned at me.

In another episode involving three members of a family who threatened suit for alleged arsenic poisoning from eating a prepared food, we obtained the records from a leading clinic where these people went for diagnosis and treatment. Hair and fingernail analyses showed repeated doses ingested over rather long intervals by these folk. The threatened lawsuit was dropped. The poisoner was never revealed nor discovered by us. Three additional episodes much like the above cases were investigated and shown to be arsenical in origin, but no legal machinery was ever set in motion so far as we know. Somehow the popular long-run play *Arsenic and Old Lace*, which we sat through in a New York theater, never amused us. As Barry Fitzgerald said in another play and in another connection, it was like "playing patty fingers in the holy water."

Though the ancient Greeks and Romans were familiar with a substance known to them as "arsenic," they were unacquainted with the free element. Their "arsenic" was a mixture of naturally occuring poisonous sulfides, which was mined by slaves at a fearful cost of life. The soluble oxides of arsenic were known, as well as arsenical pigments like orpiment (As_2S_3) and metallic arsenides. The red mineral "Armenian bole" was known, and because of its red color was used to impart color to sausages, fish pastes, confections, Pontic cherries, etc. The poisonous quality of Armenian bole was due to one thousand ppm of arsenious oxide. Many of the "slow poisonings" of ancient, medieval, and modern times were caused by repeated small doses of soluble arsenicals in food and drink. It is known that large doses are vomited and much lower mortality rates are observed. The fatal dose (calculated as As_2O_3) is 2 to 3 grains. Death occurs in one to twenty-four hours. Symptoms are not constant. There is a gastrointestinal type and a cerebrospinal type, but each person stricken presents some of the categories of each type, i.e., paralysis, stupor, vertigo, muscle spasms, neuritis, headache, and grave gastrointestinal irritation. Textbooks list other symptoms dependent upon the person and dosage of different arsenical compounds.

An interesting type of slow poisoning through inhalation of arsine gas has been observed from classical times down to the present in Rome. The conditions are as follows: arsenical pigments used in color of walls, ceilings, floors, paintings, wallpaper, statuary, etc., of bedrooms are, owing to dampness (in stone buildings) during the rainy season, subject to invisible growth of molds like *Penicillium (Scopulariopsis) brevicaulis*, and *Paecilomyces*. These molds can grow on the damp surface of the arsenical pigments and release arsine, a most poisonous gas. Bedrooms in Italy and the ancient world, as well as in modern times, were almost sealed at night because of the fear of "noxious night air," i.e. malaria. Under these conditions, rooms were observed to be death-rooms after prolonged use by a person. It is interesting also to observe a recent incident of this nature in Rome. A female United States official was slowly deteriorating physically, and the eventual diagnosis was arsenical poisoning from the environment of her bedroom. All of the ancient conditions for arsine generation were present.

The fatal doses of arsine are exposure to 50 ppm in air for one hour or exposure to 250 ppm in air for thirty minutes. These dosages are always fatal (U. S. Bureau of Mines, Technical Paper 248). Chronic poisoning by arsine leads to grave impairment of the blood-generating system. Guelman, (*J. Indust. Hygiene*, 7:6, 1925) and Tanner (*The Microbiology of Foods*, Champaign, Garrard Press, 1944, pp. 119-20) describe a biologic test for arsenic using *Penicillium brevicaulis*. This biologic

test detects the presence of 0.00001 gm of arsenic by producing the noticeable garlic odor of arsine (which ancients would
not object to). Some diethyl arsine is also produced in these
biologic reactions which some thirteen species of molds are
now known to do when growing on arsenical-containing media.

Some years ago, we visited the ancient coastlands of the
Nile delta, and Syria, Lebanon and Palestine. Below the Ladder
of Tyre at the Bay of Acre, we recalled an incident and prophecy
current when Napoleon Bonaparte invaded the Levant.

General Napoleon, not yet First Consul, marched up the
Coast in 1789, after taking Cairo. He allied himself with the
Mamelukes of Egypt and recruited 25,000 men. He told Murad
Bey, their chief, that he was a good Muslim, since "we worship
the same God." This brought out Murad's deal: The Bey demanded that Napoleon and his French army have themselves circum-
cised and Napoleon actually tried to persuade the Guard to set
an example. These bloody-handed stalwarts flatly refused on
the grounds of being opposed to bloodshed! They also implored
Napoleon to submit first to the operation. Napoleon refused
haughtily! Napoleon subjected Acre to a continuous seige for
three months with day and night bombardment. The Turks and
Syrians held fast and were relieved by the British Fleet under
Sir Sidney Smith. Napoleon and his army went into a furious
retreat—Napoleon embarking for France and his army finally
surrendering in despair. An Arab prophecy concerning Napoleon's death by poisoning came true.[92]

Napoleon Bonaparte, in his sixth year of captivity on lonely

---

[92]Napoleon's physician, Dr. Yvan, upon the request of his master, supplied
Napoleon with a packet of opium which he carried around his neck. Napoleon,
after Acre and especially after Moscow, threatened voluntary death if the situation called for suicide. He abdicated at Fontainbleau April 4, 1814 ("woe
unto him that buildeth a town with blood", as the Semites said: Hab. 11:12).
During this night he mixed the drug in water, drank it, and called his trusted
followers to his bedside. A very heavy slumber supervened accompanied by
profuse sweating. When he awoke, the symptoms had disappeared and so did
Dr. Yvan who mounted a horse already saddled and rode away at breakneck
speed. Napoleon was taken to Elba and after Waterloo was imprisoned on St.
Helena.

St. Helena in the south Atlantic (April 15, 1821), wrote his last will and testament charging that his British captors were poisoning him. He died twenty-one days later with the diagnosis of "cancer of the stomach." It has now been proven by chemical and neutron-activitation analyses of his hair (taken the day after death) that Napoleon was right. He was murdered by administration of arsenic in his food. Arsenic accumulates in hair according to the dosage and time given, and segments cut out of his hair show he had been given arsenic intermittently throughout the last year of his life.[93]

Another case of criminal arsenical poisoning came to light in 1968, also by means of neutron-activation analysis.[94] Charles Francis Hall explored the northwest coast of Greenland in 1871. The Arctic ice forced him and his fellows to put into Thank God Bay 500 miles south of the Pole. The ship's master was a Sidney Budington, and the head of the scientific staff was Emil Bessels. These men, as well as some of the crew, wanted to winter much further south, and a violent quarrel ensued. Hall became sick and died within fourteen days, maintaining that he was poisoned. The thirty members of the vessel buried him, sailed south and were rescued months afterward. Chauncey Loomis and Franklin Paddock found Hall's grave and removed samples of tissue for analysis at the Toronto Center for Forensic Sciences. The analysis showed that Hall swallowed massive doses of arsenic about two weeks before death. At this late date there is but one factual conclusion: "Hall was poisoned."

The crucial enzymes or enzyme inactivated by arsenic remains unknown, although it is known that metallic poisons including arsenic inactivate sulfhydryl groups of enzyme structures.

---

[93]*Sci. Amer.*: The perfect crime. *207*:56-58, 1962; also *Nature,* Oct. 1961.

[94]*Sci. Amer., 220*:52, 1969.

LEAD POISONING AND BIRD-SHOT
IN GAME

It would be gratuitous of us to mention more than some unique experiences and historic features encountered in lead poisoning. The literature is voluminous and accessible in many excellent toxicology books, readily available. Metallic lead and lead salts have long been known. There is a lead statuette dating from the First Dynasty of Egypt (*circa* 3100 B.C.), now in the British Museum. Lead *(plumbum)* was used by many peoples of antiquity, both as metal and salts. Lead pipes in "plumbing" and the white salts of lead for cosmetics, as well as colored salts for pigments, were widely used by the Hellenic, Hellenistic, and Roman peoples. The Roman engineers knew that lead pipes and conduits corroded and were not very suitable for potable water usage. Augustus Caesar[95] forbade the use of lead pipes for conducting potable water.

Lead is historically the most important of the metallic poisons. All forms of lead and its salts are poisonous. The Romans, at least, knew of the salts we now call carbonate, suboxide, litharge, red lead, and acetate (sugar of lead). Lead and its compounds are absorbed through the unbroken skin and of course in the gastrointestinal tract. It is an accumulative poison, i.e. eliminated very slowly, if at all.

The symptoms of acute lead poisoning vary according to dosage, but common symptoms are vomiting within thirty minutes, abdominal pain, bloody purging, headache, muscle cramps, insomnia, depression, coma, and death. In chronic or slow poisoning, there is ashen skin, lead lines on the gums (deposits of fine granules of lead sulfide), and a grave pathology of red blood cells (basophilic stippling) together with appearance of patho-

---

[95]Tanner, F. W. and Tanner, L. P.: *Food-Borne Infections and Intoxications,* 2nd ed. Champaign, Garrard Press, 1953, p. 706.

logic types of white cells. "Wrist drop" or nervous disorders are common, together with weakness, foul breath, gastrointestinal irritation and chronic nephritis.

In acute poisoning, death occurs in two to three days; in more chronic poisoning, death comes after a few weeks (depending on dosage). Postmortem findings in chronic poisoning are chiefly generalized arteriosclerosis and a contracted kidney, with general bodily changes resulting from such conditions. The smallest fatal dose of lead salts is not known but the *toxic range* is great, i.e. from acute to chronic poisoning. It has long been known that women are more susceptible to lead poisoning than men. Poisoning by lead in foods and wines is mentioned by Pliny and other Roman writers.

White lead is very poisonous when ingested and also is poisonous when applied to the unbroken skin. Even to this day in Chicago and New York, many black children who eat peeled white paint die or are stricken. (Chicago Health Dept. reports for 1960 alone show 25 deaths and about 125 cases from this cause.)

Many Athenian ladies and courtesans from classic times to the eighteen century used white lead as a face cosmetic, and the practice was widespread in Roman times among the "emancipated women of easy virtue." The use of lead-containing pewter food vessels also contributed to plumbism for a long period and was something of note in the many factors of life expectancy, especially in American Colonial times. Today, the United States Government Agencies controlling foods and cosmetics, headed by the Food and Drug Administration, decree a tolerance of less than 0.04 ppm in foods in interstate commerce.

Chronic lead poisoning or plumbism in classical times was experienced by plumbers, painters, and others exposed to metallic lead, white lead and lead paints. Wine bibblers suffered plumbism from wines and must prepared in lead vats. Red lead (minium) and red mercury salts were added to wines as color adjuvants, thus causing much illness and shortened lives of drinkers.

Theophrastos (372-288 B.C.) in his "treatise on stones" describes manufacture of white lead (Greek, *psimuthion*): "Place lead in earthenware vessel, cover with strong vinegar. It corrodes in ten days. Scrape off. Then repeat process until lead is used up. (This is sugar of lead—poisonous). Beat 'rust' into powder and boil in water for a long time, and what settles to the bottom is white lead." This is practically the process used until recently in the paint industry. Alexandrian treatises on chemistry show good diagrams of apparatuses for distillation, fusion, calcination, solution, filtrations, crystallization, water and sand baths, sublimation, etc., which certain writers erroneously attributed to the Arabs. The Arabic "alchemy" is merely the Alexandrian Greek *chemeia* with the Arabic definite article *al* prefixed.

The book *Architecture* by Vitruvius deals with the Roman chemical industries, building materials, pigments (including India ink), hygiene, metallic mercury, and other technical data. He knew of the poisonous properties of lead pipes because of the danger of lead poisoning, the symptoms of which he describes. Pliny likewise gives details of some of the chemical industries of his time, with a great deal of information concerning unguents, medicine, and lead poisons.

A few of the less-known sources of soluble lead in recent times were found in concentrated tobacco and juices which go to make up chewing snuff. Snuff plumbism was widespread for a time (1915 to 1935) until the lead arsenate pesticide was traced to the field care of the tobacco plant. Lead-lined beer vats and lead pipes from barrel to spigot were the sources for acute lead poisoning which we discovered in a metropolitan tavern (not as a customer!). Lead fumes from burning, discarded storage batteries still cause illness and fatalities in the old slum areas of Chicago (which are fast disappearing). As we noted above, black children of these areas, housed in old mansions of many cubicles where white lead-linseed oil paints were used and are now old and peeling, eat the peel and are stricken by the hundreds, with an average of twenty-five deaths each year.

Lead shot in the flesh of domesticated meat animals, game animals, squirrels, waterfowl, and upland birds has caused trouble, mostly imaginary and esthetic, among metropolitan folks who have not the tradition of old native Americans. Naturally, bird shot is found in the tissues of game when eaten, and no hunter, sportsman, or their families think anything of it. But shot (now an alloy of lead and antimony) found in market meats often leads to litigation based on an assumption that metallic poison is present or in some instances, that the foreign substance was responsible for a broken tooth. American pioneers for many generations have eaten such tissues without poisoning or other troubles. To them, the situation is likened to eating a cherry pie and finding cherry pits. But to more recent immigrants of our large cities, the situation often disturbs them and they bring lawsuits for damages. In four trials of cases in which we participated, the courts or juries have found for the plaintiffs (but then the judges and jurors were of that ethnic origin, and the judges were elected by these folk.)

Commercial meats may harbor shot, since some modern hunters appear to be quite careless when shooting. The shot cannot be detected by inspectors and thus are discovered during the meal. There were no data to the point on this problem, so we fed six rhesus monkeys 5 BBs and 10 #7.5 birdshot daily over a period of sixteen months. Complete blood pictures were made weekly, as were examinations for "lead lines" of gums, reflexes, and weight curves. Absolutely no pathology was found. Upon autopsy, the animals were normal; the tissues, gross and histologic, were normal, and findings from both chemical and spectroscopic tests for lead-antimony were comparable to tissues of normal control monkeys.

George R. Cowgill of Yale University conducted a long series of animal-feeding tests with pellets of lead and lead alloys including antimony.[96] No indications of lead poisoning were found in these pellet tests. Neither shot nor solder pellets are dangerous in this respect, but naturally these lead alloys when reduced to very fine grains and powder will, when swallowed over a period, cause plumbism.

---

[96] *J. Indust. Hygiene Toxicology*, 25, 1943; 26, 1944, (four articles).

MERCURY

Aristotle describes metallic mercury, but long before his day, the ancestors of the Syrians and Phoenicians as metallurgists "with the mark of Cain" exploring Spain, Ireland, England, and Central Europe for copper, tin, gold, and silver, encountered cinnabar or vermillion—the dark-red sulfide—and produced "quicksilver." Aristotle called mercury, *chutos arguros*, i.e. silver water. The Latins called it *hydrargyrum*. Mercury or quicksilver was known to the Greco-Roman world both as the metal or element and some of its salts as well. Their most important source was the dark red sulfide cinnabar or vermillion, mined in Iberia (Spain) and Italy. These sources still produce the major portion of the world's mercury. When cinnabar is roasted, liquid mercury is formed, with gaseous sulfur dioxide escaping into the air.

Not only mercury but also its soluble salts are exceedingly poisonous to man; liquid mercury evaporates into the air and in confined chambers or rooms is very toxic. Salivation occurs in chronic poisoning.

The toxic dose of soluble salts (except calomel which is six or more grains) is small, but lethal doses vary. Symptoms in acute poisoning appear almost at once. These are whitening of the mucus membranes, severe gastrointestinal irritation with vomiting; violent pain, bloody stools, and purging; labored respiration; rapid, thin pulse; collapse, convulsions, coma, and death. Since mercury and some of its compounds were known to the ancients, it is certain that poisoners were acquainted with its properties.

Many hundreds of cases of mercury poisoning, both grave illnesses and acute and chronic fatalities, are on record. The literature is truly voluminous and need not detain us except to note that corrosive sublimate $(HgCl_2)$ has been used for both homicidal and suicidal purposes. In two cases of suicide seen agonally, the persons suffered terrible pains, violent vomiting, bloody stools, and thready pulse. Onset may vary from three minutes to twenty minutes, and the fatal dose is often only 0.1 gm. The Food and Drug Administration prohibits all mercurial compounds, including calomel, in foods.

Before the era of Ehrlich's arsenicals for the treatment of syphilis or "lues," mercury was used as a "specific." This cure was thought to be more dangerous than the disease and evoked the European astronomers' aphorism: "Three minutes on Venus and three years on Mercury!"

ANTIMONY

Aᴺᴛɪᴍᴏɴʏ ᴘᴏɪꜱᴏɴɪɴɢ has been of rare occurrence the past few years, but during the World War I days and up to the late 1930's, this type of poisoning was all-too-frequently seen. The source of the antimony was the cheaper grades of enameled cooking utensils in which the antimony salts of the enamel were leached out in potent amounts when acid preparations like lemonade, acid fruits, and vinegared comestibles were prepared. There were many outbreaks in families and gatherings of people served lemonade, rhubarb, orange juice, and fruit preparations. Distribution of cases geographically followed the sale of these white to gray enameled wares in Canada, the United States, and Britain. Miller[97] called attention to the source in 1916, but the problem existed for another quarter of a century! "Colic" in nursing bottle-fed infants was found to be caused at times from red rubber nipples containing antimony.[98] Sulphurated antimony mixtures of oxide and sulphide were employed in the vulcanizing process which colors the rubber red-brown. There have been numerous cases of poisoning from tartar emetic (antimony-potassium tartrate). Many of these cases were accidental, but to our knowledge, twenty were homicidal and ten suicidal. Time of onset varies from a few minutes to one hour. The symptoms depend upon dosage and type of salt, but vomiting, pain, and acute illness are the striking features.

Antimony was known in ancient times in India, the Fertile Crescent including Egypt and Libya, and the later classical areas. Salts of antimony like the sulfide were used by women to darken their eyebrows. The fatal dose of a soluble antimony salt is about 1.5 grains in children and 2 grains for adults. Vomit-

---

[97]Miller, E. W.: *J. Home Econ., 8:*361, 1916.

[98]Phelps, E. B. and Stevenson, A. F.: U. S. Public Health Service, *Hyg. Lab. Bull. 96:*55, 1914.

ing is usually the first symptom, but it is known that vomiting does not follow ingestion of this poison in some cases. These latter individuals usually die in a few hours, although some adults have lingered for about ninety-six hours.

Antimony was well known to medieval alchemists and physicians who presumably inherited some of their practices from Greco-Roman times as we may infer from the medieval "Triumphal Chariot of Antimony."

A Sumerian vase of 2450 B.C. was found in Mesopotamia which, by modern chemical tests, proved to be nearly pure antimony.

CADMIUM

BEFORE WORLD WAR I, the textbooks and literature on toxicology rarely mentioned cadmium as an offender, and we were not instructed about it at all. But in the 1930's and early 1940's, cadmium poisoning came to notice in low incidence. In both Canada and the United States, cadmium-plated and cadmium utensils and ice trays were sold to the public. Here, as in the antimony enameled ware, acid foods such as lemonade, fruit jellos, and tomato juice, formed soluble salts with the metal and these were ingested. Onset of symptoms (nausea, vomiting, colic, diarrhea) occurred in fifteen to thirty minutes. Cadmium ware has been withdrawn from commerce, but sporadic cases were observed and traced to repair of culinary vessels and trays by welding with cadmium metal, according to R. F. Clapp (Public Health Service, Communicable Disease Center, Atlanta). Cadmium in the environment (air, water, food) leads to hypertension, as does zinc, which contains up to 0.5% cadmium.[99,100]

---

[99]Schroeder, H. *et al.*: *J. Chron. Dis. 20*:179, 1967.

[100]Carroll, R.: *J. A. M. A., 198*:177, 1966.

BARIUM

Barium poisoning is not often seen today, but the older literature records many cases from soluble salts of many preparations. One nonfatal case came to our attention in St. Louis, Missouri. The poisoning was caused by the carbonate—formerly used as a rodenticide—contaminating food in the household. The onset of symptoms (gastroenteritis, loss of tendon reflexes, disordered heart action and some muscle paralysis) occurred in 1.5 hours. The fatal dose of barium carbonate recorded in the literature is 10 to 12 gm, while the chloride is more toxic (fatal dose, 3 gm).

THE CYANIDES

Cyanides produced in vegetal tissues or by the chemical technologist have caused many hundreds of deaths and thousands of cases of illness. In vegetal tissues, the cassava-tapioca roots (manihot) contain much cyanide. Primal man long ago learned how to process these roots to free them of cyanide.[101] In form of glucosides, hydrocyanic acid is found in 180 species of plants! Of these vegetal sources, only the Oriental bean (*Phaseolus lunatus*) has caused fatal cases, in this hemisphere notably in Puerto Rico, where the beans are eaten. Hydrogen cyanide is liberated in the intestinal tract after ingestion (*circa* 50 mg HCN/100 gm of bean).

Accidental poisonings from cyanides in certain silver polishes have been seen, but most recorded poisonings are suicidal (cyanides and the gas taken by jewelers, pharmacists, chemists, and photographers). Numerous Nazis ended their careers with cyanide in capsules and pills.

Fumigation with cyanide gas was a standard practice for many years. One nearly fatal case in a colored foreman of fumigation near Norfolk, Virginia occurred about thirty years ago. After long experience with acids plus alkali cyanide pellets in tubs placed in rooms of industrial establishments and ships' holds, this good man entered a gassed room before it was thoroughly ventilated. ("Old timers" usually smoked a cigarette—the peculiar, distinctive taste of the tobacco smoke in rooms containing toxic amounts of hydrogen cyanide was a supposed warning). Falling to the floor, he was carried out to fresh air and pronounced dead by the hurriedly summoned physician. His employer instituted artificial respiration and kept it up for just over four hours when the stricken man "waked

---

[101] Jensen, L. B.: *Man's Foods: Nutrition and Environments in Food-Gathering Times and Food-Producing Times.* Champaign, Garrard Press, 1953, p. 166-167.

up," sick and dizzy—nothing else! Asked how it felt to be dead, he replied that he "just slept for a spell and saw no Bible people."

Cyanide is the enzymatic system poisoner par excellence. Lethal dosages vary. *Per os,* the fatal dose of hydrogen cyanide is 1 grain; of potassium or sodium cyanide it is 2 to 10 grains with very rapid onset.

A case of alleged homicide in the 1920's became well known to the public through a story of the murder and trial published by the now defunct *Liberty Magazine.* A college boy allegedly gave his pregnant sweetheart some cyanide, whereupon the poor girl promptly died. After some investigations and finally in the trial of the case, it was proven that the boy had access to sodium cyanide in his college chemistry laboratory. As the testimony inched on, the coroner's chemist testified that he found cyanide in the girl's tissues in large amounts. The question was then directed to him to state whether it was potassium or the sodium salt. The toxicologist said potassium but added that the cyanide radical was the deadly poison—not sodium or potassium. Since it was alleged that the defendant had access only to sodium cyanide (the reagent bottle in evidence as exhibit), the attorney for the defendant made a great heart-rending exhortation to the jury who thereupon found the lad not guilty! These laymen set great store on the crucial differences between "soda (natrium) and potash (kalium)" (or was the chemical substance gold or silver?)

We recall a story of a cyanide case in Kansas City before World War I which provided some satisfaction for the toxicologist testifying as expert witness for the state. This witness, easily the outstanding toxicologist of the day, was Dr. Walter Stanley Haines, Coroner's Chemist of Cook County and professor of toxicology and medical jurisprudence in Rush Medical College. His testimony was being broken up by a torrent of interrupting logomachy from the other side in the case. The court had qualified him as an expert. When Dr. Haines could no longer clarify his subject, his attorney wrangled out a stipulation from the other side to the effect that Dr. Haines could tell all he knew about cyanides without interruption if he did not resort to repetition. The court agreed and, upholding the stipulation, permitted the doctor to proceed. Dr. Haines testified for two days without repeating himself (10:00 A.M. to 12:00 noon, 1:30 P.M. to 4:30 P.M.) at a fee of $200.00 per day—a huge sum in those times. The other side had studies made of the court reporter's transcript, but no repetitive statements were found.

SODIUM FLUORIDE

Sodium fluoride was long used as a household insecticide for roaches, ants, and other arthropods. After World War II, the use of DDT and a long list of new insecticides rendered the more dangerous fluoride obsolete for this purpose. White fluoride powder has caused many outbreaks of food poisoning. Most states have passed laws requiring the compound to be colored green or blue so that it would not be accidentally used as "flour, baking soda, or powdered milk."

Symptoms of poisoning from sodium fluoride have been confused with botulism. We shall cite an example of this confusion directly. After ingestion of this poison in food, the onset was sudden in the cases seen by us. Gastrointestinal reaction was violent; convulsions, muscle spasms, paresis of muscles and ptosis are confusing to those who have never seen a case of botulism.

The outbreak which we shall describe was a wretched affair for all concerned. Ten men from a war plant ate at an adjacent wartime restaurant. This noon meal consisted of ordinary foods with "sweetbreads" or calf thymus which had been "floured" and fried. Two men died at table and the rest who were stricken were taken to a small hospital where the autopsied dead were "signed out" in the death certificate as "died from botulism!" The eight men eventually recovered. The widows of the two deceased men sued the restaurant owner who impleaded the vendor store but failed to implead the purveyor who had no place of business here. (The vendor merchant corporation eventually sued the purveyor for recovery of moneys spent in these cases).

Investigating this outbreak, we by chance interrogated the nine-year-old daughter of the cook who told us, "I ate the sweetbreads fried without that white flour that we are not supposed to talk about to anyone." The hospital "pathologist" stuck doggedly to his diagnosis of botulism, and the cause of death in these cases was listed in the statistics as botulism. After legal wrangling and mistrials, the lawsuits of all who sued were settled out of court. We found the fluoride in a remnant of the food and vomitus, but we were not permitted to see the autopsy report or the forensic chemistry of tissues from autopsy. Here again the old uncolored insecticide was somehow introduced into the flour used for covering the fried food.

SULFITES AND 4,000-YEAR-OLD
PRESERVED MEAT AT JERICHO

THERE IS A LARGE literature on the use of sulfites in foods. Almost universal condemnations have been voiced officially on the use of sulfites in meats. The temperate use of sulfites and sulfur dioxide to protect fruits and vegetables often has been viewed, both in theory and practice, as beneficial and harmless. Nichols[102] presented evidence in favor of the harmlessness of sulfites used in the drying of fruits. The average amounts used were given as between 2,000 and 3,000 ppm for apricots, peaches, and pears. Tanner[103] writes that "results of investigations suggest that the sulfur dioxide has a destructive effect upon thiamin, but not on vitamin A or ascorbic acid, retention of which is indeed improved. Restrictive limitations against sulfur dioxide retention are not required or should be liberal."

Fitzhugh, Knudsen, and Nelson[104] of the Federal Food and Drug Administration conclude that these sulfur preservatives may possess some chronic toxicity in levels of 1000 ppm (sodium hydrogen sulfite), but 0.25 per cent produced histopathologic changes. Much of the pathology was considered to be due to destruction of thiamine, which is readily destroyed by sulfites.

Hoppe and Goble[105] determined the toxicity of sodium bisulfite by intravenous injection into experimental animals. Naturally, the data from this type of study are not comparable to feeding tests. The LD_{50} (milligram per kilogram) of bisulfite, sulfite, and sulfate in distilled water were found to be:

---

[102]Nichols, C. W.: *Amer. J. Public Health, 24*:1129-1134, 1934.
[103]Tanner, F. W.: *Microbiology of Foods.* Champaign, Garrard Press, 1944, p. 34.
[104]Fitzhugh, O. G., et al.: *J. Pharm. Exp. Ther. 86*:37-48, 1946.
[105]Hoppe, J. O., and Goble, F. C.: *J. Pharm. Exp. Ther. 101*:101-106, 1951.

Sodium	bisulfite	mouse	130 ± 8
Sodium	bisulfite	rat	115 ± 10
Sodium	bisulfite	hamster	95 ± 6
Sodium	bisulfite	rabbit	65
Sodium	sulfite	mouse	175 ± 6
Sodium	sulfate	mouse	1220 ± 90

Hoppe and Goble found no evidence of cumulative toxicity by intravenous injection of sodium bisulfite in a subacute toxicity study in rabbits (120 mg/kg), five days a week for three weeks.

Sodium sulfite USP is used in treating humans in fermentative dyspepsia in dosages of 0.3 to 1. 3 gm.[106]

Sollman[107] stated, "In man, one gram (of sodium sulfite) produced no effects; four to six grams caused violent colic, diarrhea, and circulatory disturbances. It oxidizes in air to sulfate."

Dunn and Highlands[108] state that during World War II, cabbage received 750 to 1500 ppm of sodium sulfite; carrots, 500 to 1000 ppm; and white and sweet potatoes 200 to 500 ppm.

The Council on Foods, American Medical Association, states, "small quantities of sulfur dioxide are not objectionable in fruit products, provided the quantity does not exceed that compatible with good manufacturing practice."[109]

We noted above that sulfites should never be used as a preservative and color restorative in meats. This refurbishing practice has a long history behind it, but in recent years the reducing vitamin derivatives have been used as color adjuvants and restorers.

It will be recalled that the myoglobin of muscle may take up oxygen, thus brightening the meat a few hours after cutting the slaughtered product. When myoglobin, the residual red pigment of meat, is long exposed to air or oxidized by bacterial action, a series of color reactions occur: myogloblin (hemoglobin

---

[106]*U. S. Dispensatory,* 1950 edition, p. 1096.

[107]Sollman, Torrald: *A Manual of Pharmacology,* Philadelphia, Saunders, 1948, p. 129.

[108]Dunn, C., and Highlands, M. E.: *Food Technol. 1,* 133-141, 1947.

[109]*Accepted Foods and Their Nutritional Significance.* Chicago, American Medical Association, 1939. p. 85, and 186.

of red cells act similiarly) oxidized to brown (metmyoglobin), then greenish colors are eventually produced (choleglobin).[110] This oxidation process may be prevented by reducing agents like sulfites, or if the oxidized unwanted colors have formed, the addition of sulfite often reduces the oxidized derivatives back to red.

The practice is harmful because it may mask a vicious original condition due to bacterial growth. If *Staphylococcus* enterotoxin had formed and slightly oxidized, the reducing action of sulfites tends to cause manifold increases in toxicity as noted in outbreaks and our laboratory tests. The sulfite often diminishes in content, being oxidized to sulfate. A District of Columbia health officer, some twenty-five years ago, pointed out some of these dangers in a mimeographed bulletin. Spoiled meat products like cured varieties of sausage also tend to become deodorized as uncured meats.

We cite one example of "devious pathways" of the old sulfite process for meats. In 1938, a group of small sausage–kitchen operators worked up a bill for legalizing the use of sulfites, calling it the "poor man's refrigerant." At a midwestern State general assembly, the bill, came upon the floor for passage. We were commissioned to prevent passage, since the process reflected on the food industry. Obtaining some ground pork and ground beef, we held these comminuted meats in our hot hotel room overnight. The meats became discolored and "off-odor." Then, after some difficult procedures, we finally were admitted to the state governor's presence. Stating our mission and proposed experiment, we added a solution of sodium sulfite to the meats which became red and greatly deodorized. Observing this, His Excellency, the late Governor Horner of Illinois, phoned the floor leader and directed that the bill be buried "so deep that it would never come up again." Thanking His Excellency, we lost no time getting out of that city. The bill was killed aborning!

Sulfur dioxide (SO_2) gas, when used in small-plant refrig-

---

[110]Jensen, L. B.: *Microbiology of Meats,* 3rd ed. Champaign, Garrard Press, 1954, Ch. III, IV, and colored plate (p. 176).

eration devices, has been observed to escape and cause surface darkening of fresh beef.[111]

While visiting Syria and Palestine some years ago, we learned of a very ancient effect of sulfites on preservation of meat, which may be of interest. At Jericho, the oldest city known, the latest excavation done there by Kathleen Kenyon[112,113] has revealed a walled town almost fifty feet below the city that Joshua was credited with taking. This surprisingly ancient town with "polished floors," according to repeated carbon 14 datings (of charcoal found there in two levels) was flourishing about 6250 B.C. to 5850 B.C., and in the settlement below this level were found brick houses—beehive shaped—and the earliest town-wall known. This massive stone-walled town carries us back to the seventh millennium and shows a society organized in larger units than dreamed of by the most daring archaeologists of a few years ago.

The Jericho village began about 10,000 years ago and as Miss Kenyon has written, "It has already been established that a date of *circa* 6000 B.C. was comparatively late in the history of Neolithic Jericho."

As the great archeologist, Dr. Nelson Glueck, said long ago, "And in the beginning there was Jericho" (Tell es-Sultan). Jericho then connects with the neolithic Natufian period of the Mt. Carmel caves!

Miss Kenyon, in the 1953 and 1954 excavations, found some 4,000-year-old burial chambers with much grave goods. With each skeleton lay a dagger, both on a wooden bier. Diffusing sulfur gases from this old volcanic and rift area (sulfur dioxide, sulfites, and hydrogen sulfide) preserved the wood, woven cloth, and *meat offerings*. These meats were dehydrated with some carbonization and had undergone microbial action during and

---

111Jensen, L. B.: *Microbiology of Meats,* 3rd ed. Champaign, Garrard Press, 1954, p. 180.

112Kenyon, Kathleen: *Digging up Jericho.* London, 1957. (Discoveries which revolutionize archeology and chronology of Canaan and urban development).

113Kenyon, Kathleen: *Archeology in The Holy Land.* New York, Praeger, 1957.

soon after burial. Liquors remained in the jars. There were stools, couches, jugs, plates, baskets, and cosmetics for the women. As mentioned above, these sulfur compounds, called "the poor man's refrigerant" by modern charlatans who add sulfites illegally, of course, to meats, are good for the Jericho archaeologists but ruined the digestion of Occidental peoples where the inspectors were not vigilant. Nowadays other compounds have been designed for these uses, but modern technology has largely obviated the need for such practices.

A FLEETING NOTE ON ANCIENT TEMPLE MEATS FROM SACRIFICES

W HILE IN THE LEVANTINE countries, we recalled lectures in Egyptology and Near East history in classes during our youth and somehow remembered the animal sacrifices to the gods of the Ancient World. Torrents of blood and myriads of animals—oxen, sheep, lambs, goats and doves—were sacrificed in Mesopotamian, Syrian, Hellenic, Hellenistic, and Roman temples to gain favor with the gods and to obtain some prognostication for good or evil in human activities.

These pagan rites are described quite fully in the ancient surviving records. The Hebrew rites are not so generally well known; hence we delved into the subject with the point of view of pragmatic technology rather than theology. Here is a summary of what we found in the literature and on the sites.

When Solomon dedicated his Temple, he sacrificed 120,000 sheep and lambs. After the Babylonian Captivity, the Jews who returned to Judea and Jerusalem constructed a poorer edifice on the site and continued the blood sacrifices. With the building of the great white Temple of Herod, the practices became a huge, well-organized obsession. To the credit of the Hebrews, they abhorred the Aztec-like Moloch sacrifices of their predecessors, the Canaanites, and followed the dictates of Jehovah or Yaweh from which some of the world's noble religions evolved.

Killing of animals and man in ritual was an age-old Neolithic practice to propitiate the gods or God and for divination of events or prognosis. This wanton slaughter was an abomination to Jesus and his fellow Jews, and also to St. Paul and Johanan Ben Zakkai. When the Temple was destroyed by Titus in 70 A.D., Johanan Ben Zakkai and his followers fled by Roman sanction to Jamnia where his new Jewish ethics of the synagogue became the seed of a nobler religion which has evolved to this day.

185

Both Jesus and Johanan rejected this pagan ritual which both Jew and gentile had believed a measure for bringing men closer to God.

The Passover of 64 A.D. is illustrative of this ritual. Every road to Jerusalem was crowded with Jews and their sheep or lambs shepherded and carried templewards. Cestius Gallus, governor of Syria, informed Nero of the animals slain as being 256,500. Flavius Josephus intimates a larger number for the Paschal of 69 A.D., and with "oriental preciseness" reckons 2,700,200 people in Jerusalem and environs for this Passover. (About 1,100,000 Jews were killed by Jewish terrorists and Romans in the war of 66 to 70 A.D.). At the north gate of the Temple terrace, called the "Gate of the Sheepfold," were assembled the huge numbers of sheep for the slaughter. They filled not only the western half of this court but extended outside of the city wall to the north through the Tadi Gate. What bleating and blowing of silver trumpets, horns, etc.! On ordinary days, the priests sacrificed and burned a few animals and mutton fat on the Altar of Sacrifice.

On the afternoon of the day in which the Passover was observed, the Passover lambs were killed for sacrifice and the Passover meal. The blood representing life belonged to God and was caught in bowls of silver and gold and passed rapidly by hand to the priest nearest the altar where it was tossed against the base before coagulation. Actually, two long rows of barefoot priests were the "assembly line" in the sacrifice, one row holding golden vessels, the other silver, each passing forward the blood and passing back the empty bowls. The kosher killers handed the filled bowls to the two rows of priests ((Mishnah, Pesahim 5.5 (Danby)). The sheep were then flayed and eviscerated while fat burned on the altar. The pelt was kept by the priests as a partial payment for the service. The animal-sacrifice altar and eight marble tables where the animals were flayed were provided with a blood drain near the southwest corner of the altar. The vicinity of this altar was much like a butcher's slaughter house with areas for tethering animals, washing them, and washing the blood-drenched priests who sacrificed. Slaughter of the sheep was conducted at the Place of Slaughter behind the altar and Porch and Court of the Israelites. The killing began at 1:30 P.M. and ceased at sunset. What a scene that must have been and what organization!

Daily, for long centuries, sacrifices, routine and special, went on in a never-ending bloody stream. Thousands of private individuals offered sheep, goats, and oxen as substitutes for God's favor. While the priests caught the blood and often ate the meats, the ordinary Jew was given no spiritual direction but rather was fleeced with his sheep. Isaiah cried out against the bloody practice.

The disposal of torrents of blood at the base of the altar would present a problem even now in this age of sanitary engineering. The volume of whole blood in kosher killing is greater than gentile slaughter of food animals (beef, lamb, or sheep). A thirty-pound animal (sacrificial animals were often heavier) contains 8 per cent blood or 2.4 pounds. Twelve pounds of serum equates with 1.5 gallons of fluid (not blood cells, fibrin). Hence, 256,500 lambs would shed 51,300 gallons of serum (more if whole blood is reckoned.) This "torrential stream" of highly putrescible blood would create a stench problem for any temple, and it is significant that huge quantities of incense were burned as a deodorant to "mask the effluvia!" The whole mass was sluiced off with water drawn up by a water wheel with ropes and pails from the huge cisterns under the whole temple platform. The largest of these reservoirs was called the Great Sea and held two million gallons of water.

Both the blood thrown on the altar by priests in Jesus' time and the wash water drained in channels down the Rock, and today these channels can be traced when you go down to a cavern. In this cavern or cave is a floorstone that rings hollow when struck and some passage is beneath it, but Muslim refusal of permission to search is as adamant as the inscription on the ancient temple tile recovered years ago (1873) in the temple precincts (now in Constantinople Museum) warning "Gentiles who enter here will be killed."

There are known great reservoirs, cisterns, passageways,

and defilement washrooms under the esplanade of the Mount of Zion now the Dome of the Rock, but Muslim refusal of permission to search and excavate leaves one of the intriguing mysteries of Biblical archaeology unanswered. Possibly, but not likely, many of the sacred relics of the Temple, including the true golden menorah, as well as the Ark of the Covenant, are there.

The outfall is said to go into the Valley of Kedron, but other local commentators say it goes into the Valley of Hinnon or Gehenna. Gehenna, the symbol of Hell, has always been a place execrated by Jew, Christian, and Muslim and was also the garbage dump even in the days of the kings of Judah. Nearby is the field of blood (Aceldama)—the potter's field where Judas Iscariot was buried. The Hinnon valley dump, like such places in all historic time, was always smoldering with evil smoke from its refuse. The daily summer temperature accentuated these conditions.

Many ancient and medieval cities reeked with odors offensive to modern nostrils like the ancient Esquiline dump in Rome excavated some time ago by Professor Lanciani whose hardy workmen were overcome by the viscid, horrid mess.[114] The humans of ancient times, like most of us in the trenches during World War I, developed anosmia, i.e. an absence of a keen sense of smell!

After the Crucifixion, when the Christian movement accelerated in vigor, the ancient Jewish Code of the Jewish Christians regulating meats was a stumbling block to the Pauline gentile converts. Eating of meats of animals sacrificed to idols, blood, and the meats of animals butchered without having been previously kosher bled was abominable to the Jews and many Christians. In pagan communities of the Roman Empire, it was no easy thing to distinguish market meats from the huge daily supply from sacrifices at the pagan temples. Ex-pagans attached little importance to the prohibition, and both Paul and Peter had much to do to see that Christian ritualistic (agape) meals were

---

[114]Lanciani, Rodolfo: *Ancient Rome.* Houghton-Mifflin, Boston, 1889. Recent writers question this, but contemporaries, both Italian and American residents of Rome, saw and smelled this awful pit.

kosher. (Rom. 14; 1 Cor. 10:23). The Apostolic Decree spot-
lighted "scandals" right down through the Middle Ages—especially eating blood sausages and "black puddings." Eusebius
cites examples of martyrs (Lyons, 177 A.D.) who would not eat
"blood."

Many ancient writers describe bull's blood and goat's blood
as very toxic when ingested and thought, as did St. Augustine
of Hippo, that it was used as a poison. The rites and theology
of Mithra which competed with early Christianity employed
bull's blood to "bless" (in Latin, bless means "sprinkled with
blood") and was considered "potent and mysterious." Modern
examinations of bull's blood reveal no exceptional properties so
far as toxicology is concerned. Teutonic nations have made
"black puddings" of blood for ages without experiencing alimentary discomfort. Esthetic discomfort might be involved in
case of other peoples. However, the classical Greeks ate black
puddings with great relish.

When Abraham migrated (about 2000 B.C.) from Mesopotamia (Ur of the Chaldees which Sir Leonard Wooley (1950)
and others excavated and through which they restored for us
the everyday life of the city of Abraham), he and his people
had adopted and borrowed many food practices of the Valley.
Today the Euphrates runs ten miles east of the ruins of Ur, and
the great plain is a barren desert. It is not known when the
river changed its course.

The ancient Jewish food practices, so remarkable when
viewed with microbiologic and nutritional knowledge of today,
need intensive study of the source material. Their basic foods
were much like the foods elsewhere in the Fertile Crescent,
but their preparations and choice of foods were rigidly controlled through keen observation and retention of experience.
Wheat and barley groats were cooked with cut-up tender lamb
or morsels of mutton, together with many kinds of vegetables.
Other foods were beans, lentils, peas, onion, leeks, garlic, fish,
dairy foods, wheat, barley, lucerne, dates, figs, grape, apples,
mulberries, Persian peaches, eggplant, melons, cucumbers, tur-
nips, radishes, sesame, vegetable oils, mint, cardamons, pennyroy-

al, dill, saffron, coriander, thyme, mangold, lettuce, and beer and wine. Olives and oil, grapes and raisins, honey and dates (taking the place of sugar), almonds, walnuts, apples, pears, pomegranates, and figs were staples. In the sixth century B.C., fowl and eggs (chickens, ducks, geese) became important items of diet. Beef, selected and trimmed according to code was used extensively.

In the book of Leviticus, Chapter 11, and Deuteronomy, Chapter 14, the Code of Moses given to the Israelites lists the, animals, fish, birds, and insects that can be eaten and under what conditions they can be eaten. It is forbidden to eat the meat of the pig, camel, and horse, and the shrimp, lobster, oyster, and crab. Meat must be produced according to code and must meet health standards. Because of pagan prebiblical customs, meat foods and dairy foods could not be eaten together. Animals of the chase were usually forbidden. The great physician-philosopher, Maimonides, long ago pointed out that the Kosher Code restrictions were health measures, particularly in case of pork which may be parasitized and which spoils rapidly in warm climates. He pointed out also that there are moral values to be gained from restraint in eating habits, and discrimination in satiety reflects on self-control with other of life's temptations.

Qualified students, both historians with a pragmatic bias and theologians as well, might glean something useful from the science of nutrition when they attempt to explain the cause of the extraordinary influence of Palestine on world history. Israel never adopted foreign practices and ideas until they proved their worth and could be assimilated without sacrificing autonomy of spirit. Until the nutritional patterns of the Jews from Ibrahim Khalil Abdurrahman, the friend of God, down to recent times is revealed by patient research, we may anticipate much of interest.

Sir Frederick Gowland Hopkins of Cambridge thought no nation in history had ever been fed on a properly balanced diet. We have concrete evidence that the Jews, with their dietary habits rigidly controlled by regulation, may have experienced selection of individuals during the centuries, but at the same time their food selection has saved countless members from the ravages of malnutrition, parasitic worms, bacteria, and epidemic plagues. Food has played as important a role in human character as climate, although the two were hopelessly intertwined before the advent of rapid and refrigerated transport.

The Bible, as well as archaeology, shows that in the ninth century B.C., Israelite women no longer depended upon the nearest spring or stream for water, but that every house had its own cistern where the winter rainfall was stored for use throughout the year. Cleanliness and sanitation were rigidly practiced according to the Mosaic Law. Albright has proved by the evidence of archaeology that emphasis on personal hygiene and avoidance of bad food practices which spread disease were their way of life. Cisterns were provided with settling basins for clarification of the water, even though the rainwater was collected from the rooftops. The ordinary household actually lived in the upper story of their home, not the ground floor, which was used for storage and work quarters. Underground drains were found in all towns of the interior. The common people of an ancient Jewish village washed their hands before eating, and the taking of frequent baths was imposed by law. Such sanitary practices, together with observance of the Mosaic Code and later admonitions, must surely have saved many people from illness and untimely death.

INDEX

A

Aconite, 135-136
  aconitine and 5 additional alkaloids, 135
  aconite in Juvenal's Rome, 135
  distribution of plant, 135
  extreme toxicity, 135
  name derives from port of Acone on Black Sea, 135
  not used as medicine, 135
  Phraates murders his father, 135-136
Alcoholic beverages in ancient times, 117-121
  beaker makers-Neolithic racketeers, 121
  beer, wheats, barleys, 117
  Celtic (Gallic) thirst for wine, 121
  distribution of poisonous nectars, 120-121
  Egyptian drinking "parlors", 117
  Hugulu's mongols' invasion of the Near East, 118, 141
  mead, 119-121
    from poisonous honey, 120-121
  Mohamet's ban on wine, beer, mead, 117-118
  Philistines, barley beer drinkers, 121
  poisonous additives in wines, 118-119, 166
  Punic strong wines, 118
  "Symposium", Greek and Roman drinking dinner, 117
  wines, 116-120
  Xenophon's "Ten Thousand" stricken, 120
  Yassa, Gengis Khan's Code on strong drink, 118
Anaerobes in battle wounds, France 1914-1918, 36
Antibiotic induced colitis, 54-55

Antidotes for Poisons, 112-114
  "bezoars" in ancient Near East, China, Peru, 112
  "cure-all" (theriac), most famous ever known, 113
  ingredients of European and Venetion theriac, 111-113
  King Mithridates recipe of 63 ingredients, 112-113
  snake handling sects and primal Christians, 114
  theriac ingredients worthless, 112-113
  theriac or *Mithridaticum,* 112-115
  theriac used from 70 A.D.-1860 A.D. still compounded and sold in Venice (1960), 114
  "treacle", Venetian theriaca, 113-114
  Tycho's theriac with antimony, 157
Antimony, 171-173
  colic in infants from rubber nipples containing, 171
  fatal dose, 171
  poisoning from enamel wares, 171
  poisoning from tartar emetic, 171
  Sumerian vase of pure antimony, 172
  Triumphal Chariot of Antimony, 172
  uses in Ancient Times, 171
Appomattox campaign, foods in, 13
Arsenic, 158-165
  Armenian bole, arsenic in, 161
  arsenic compound mistakenly used as flour, 160-161
  arsenic in the Classical World, 161, 162
  arsenic in pigments and mold growth producing arsine gas, 162

Cicero against Oppianicus (Pro Cluentio), 159
defendant lawyers, 159-160
fatal dose, 162
fatal dose of arsine, 162
hair and fingernail analyses for, 161, 164
minute quantities detected by mold growth, 162
murder of Charles Francis Hall with arsenic, 164
murder of Napoleon by arsenic, 164
neutron-activation analyses for arsenic, 164
poisoning by arsenic, banquet for Archbishop M., 160
symptoms in poisoning with arsenic, 162
trial of a case involving arsenic, 158, 159
Assassins and *Cannabis Indica-Sativa,* 139-143
Baybars destroys Syrian assaassins, 139
Cannabis called marihuana, 141
drug effects, 142
founding of terrible cult on Elburz range, 139
"hashish", (Arabic) drug, 139, 141-142
hemp smoking in ancient Scythia, 142
Hulugu, mongol chief exterminates Elburz assassins, 141
Ismailites of Aga Khan, 139, 140, 141
marihuana, 141-142
murderers drugged with Cannabis, 139
Muslim schizmatic sects, 139
Old Man of the Mountains, 139
potent Mexican and Far East varieties, 142
Saladin, attempted murder of, 140
tables of organization of Assassins, 139
Attorneys, 159-160 (*see* Trials of cases or Lawsuits)

B

Barium, 173
carbonate formerly a rodenticide, 173
fatal dose (carbonate), 173
non-fatal case, 173
symptoms of poisoning, 173
Beer in Ancient Times, 117-121
Belladonna, 125
alkaloids of, 125
distribution, 125
fatal dose, 125
instillations in ear or eye fatal, 125
poisoner in Hamlet, 125
Bezoars or gallstones as medicine in China, Near East, Peru, 112
Bird-shot in game, 167-168
Botulism
acidity inhibits spore germination, 69
action of toxins, 67
avidity for nerve tissues, 65-66
brine concentration inhibits spore germination, 69
canned foods (commercial), 64-65
cold pack methods and, 64-65
discovery, 64
ethyl alcohol, effects on toxins, 69-72
neurotoxins, 64, 65, 67, 68, 71
neutralization of toxin by specific antitoxins, 65, 66
oil intrapment of spores, 67
resistant spores in soil, 66, 67
sausages (Latin, *botulus*), 64
spores, time-temperature for kill, 66-67
symptoms, 67, 69
time-temperatures nullifying toxins, 68
toxicity, 71
types of *C. botulinum,* 65
type E, "Marine toxin", 68
a typical case, 69
washed spores innocuous, 67
Brine concentrations inhibitory for germination of *C. botulinum* spores, 69

Brucellosis, 90
  brucella in deep tissues of kid or
      calf boiled in colostrum, 90
  species, 90
Buffalo (Bison) meat and illness, 18
Bull's blood and goat's blood, 155, 189
Bull run, 9-10
  battle of, 9
  General McDowell's suffering, 10
  General Pope's headquarters, 10

C

Cadmium, 173-174
  in environment leads to hyperten-
      sion, 173
  poisoning from utensils and ice tray
      made with, 173
  symptoms of poisoning with, 173
  in zinc, 173
Canned Foods, 9
  botulism, 64, 66, 68, 69
  in Civil War, 9
  in Napoleonic Wars, 33
Carbon monoxide, 146-151
  in air of city streets, 146
  in ancient kiln and smelter fuels,
      149
  deaths in Ancient Rome, due to,
      148-149
  effects of carbon monoxide, 145,
      146, 147, 148, 149
  effects simulate food poisoning,
      146-147
  refrigeration gases, 146
Cascara buckthorn in Indian wars, 20
Castor bean poisons, 131-133
  circumglobal in cultivation, 131
  fatalities, 131
  Mussolini's use of castor oil as a
      judicial public purge, 132
  poisoning in Oklahoma and lower
      Mississippi valley, 131
  poisons in *Ricinus Communis*
    ricin, as protein (antigenic), 131
    ricinine, an alkaloid, 131
  toxic and allergic action of whole
      bean, 131

toxic dose of ricinine very small,
    131
uses by Egyptians and Babylonians,
    131
varieties, 131
Cave of Bats and Opium, 133
Cheyenne Indians, cholera deaths, 18
Cigarettes, 144
Civil War, the, 8-15
  Appomattox Campaign, foods in, 13
  army rations in, 11, 15
  army standards for salted beef, 14
  beans, "half baked", 12
  Bull Run, battles, 9, 10
  canned foods, in, 9
  descriptive names for dysenteries,
      8, 11
  dysenteries, descriptive names of, 7
  extent of dysenteries in CSA, 10, 11
  food poisoning bacteria in, 9 ff
  gastrointestinal diseases, 8, 9
  hardtack "worm castles", 12, 14
  morbidity rates, in, 9
  mortality rates, in, 9
  "Nassau bacon", 13
  National Hotel Disease, in, 13
  "potable water" and diseases, 11
  Salmonella, 9
  salted meat, 11, 14
  sanitary sciences in, 8
  shadow soup, 12
  Shigella, 9
  Shiloh, 11, 12-13
  sutlers' wares, 8
  U. S. Grant's food habits, 13
  veterans' attitudes, 8
Cleopatra's poison tests using humans,
    125
Clostridium perfringens, 71-73
  food poisoning outbreaks due to, 72
  onset of symptoms, 71, 72
  symptoms in outbreaks, 71-72
  times-temperatures for spore kill,
      71-72
Colchicine (Colchium), 137-138
  alkaloid, colchicine very poisonous,
      137
  autumn crocus (C. *autumnale*),
      137

habitat, 137
murders with seeds, 137
not toxic for Syrian hamsters, 137-138
symptoms, 137
Conium maculatum, 121, 123
Cyanides, 175-177
 accidental poisoning, 175
 lethal dosage, 176
 manihot (tapioca) roots, in, 175
 a non-fatal case in fumigation, 175
 poisoning from Oriental bean in Puerto Rico, 175
 180 species of plants, in, 175
 trial of a case and outcome, 175

D

Damascus sword steel, preparation of, 46
Defendant attorneys, 159, 160
Diamond (powdered in food and drink), 154-155
 Benvenuto Cellini's experience with, 154-155
 diamonds in Roman times, 155
 other gems and ceramics, effects of, 154
 historical cases of "slow poisoning", 155-157
 as a slow poison, 155-157
 "slow poison" debate, 155, 157
Dinoflagellate poisons, 67, 95
Dysenteries in Civil War, 8, 9, 11

E

Elburz range (Assassins), 139, 141
Encephalitis, 24
Enterointoxication in pancake-waffle batters, 52
Ergotism, outbreak in Caesar's Legion, 30, 31
Escherichia coli, serologic O11B₄ and 055B₅ in diarrhea, 80
Esparto cloth, baskets, 133
Ethyl alcohol and botulism, 69-72
Eutron®, effects of tryramine with pressor compound, 62
Extinction of passenger pigeon, 23, 24

F

Foods in the Past, 26-30
 ancient Egyptian baker, 27
 Caesar's food logistics in Gaul, 30
 Cyprian salami, 28
 ergot outbreak in a legion, 30-31
 food poisoning in German troops at Verdun, 31
 Greek sausage, 28
 leprosy and spoiled foods, 29
 meat inspection wardens, London, 29
 Parisian sausage, 28
 Piers Plowman on punishments, 28
 poisoner on Legion staff, 31
 posca, legionnaire beverage, 30
 rations of Caesar's legions, 30
 Roman military camps, 31
 ropy bread in 13th century London, 27
 St. Paul's illness in Galatia, 29
 Serratia marcescens and "blood", 27-28
Food-borne Viral Diseases, 73-77
 Chicago Stockyards fire, infections, 76
 heat resistances, 74
 hepatitis, viruses of, 74
 intestinal viruses, F.S. and Marcy, 73
 outbreaks of infectious hepatitis, 74-75

G

Genus Bacillus, 71
 food poisoning due to, 52, 71
 incubation period for onset, 71
 sweet curdling of milk, 71
Glass in food and drink, 151-154
 dog experiments with glass, 152
 foreign substances in foods, 151
 glass in foods, 151
 law suits, 152-154
Grant, Ulysses S., foods, 13
Greco-Roman world, poisoners, 105-112
 Arminius (Herman, Armand), 107

Cos, altar of Asclepius and Opollo, 110
crude drugs sold in Rome, 109
cup bearers and tasters, 107
drugs, poisons and preparation, 105-107
Josephus on poisonings, 109
"Judicial treatment" of poisoners by Medes and Persians, 107
mineral poisons available, 106-107
pharmacists of Pompeii, 109
physicians of ancient times, 105, 108-109
poisonous plants, cultivation, 106
professional poisoners, 110-111
Tacitus on poisoning — excerpts, 107-108
useful drugs employed by physicians, 105, 109-110
Vavilov's researches, 106

H

Hamlet, instillation of poison in ear, 125
Hamsters, 137-138
discovery of, in 1839, 138
uses in researches, 138
Hardtack, 12, 14, n. 5
Harvard Medical School, 8
first microscope at, 8
Professor Horsford's meat ration, 22
Hemlock: the Socratic poison, 121-124
agonal period in Socrates, 122
ancient descriptions of, 123
Conium maculatum: distribution of, 121, 123
death of Aristotle, 122
death of Seneca, 122
death of Socrates, 121-122
death of Therames, 122
as a judicial poison, 121-123
poisoning in American children, 122-123
principle alkaloid, coniine, 122
quail meat containing the poison, 123
Hemp, *C. indica,* 142

Henbane, 126
alkaloids: hyoscyamine and Scopolamine, 126
Egyptian, *H. muticus* very poisonous, 126
Hyoscyamus niger, 126
parsley, confused with, 126
Herodotus' (Book IV) description of Scythians, hemp smoking, 142
Horse meat and dysenteries, 21, 22
Human volunteers
Salmonella tests, 56
with other bacteria, 81
staphylococcal enterotoxin 34, 35, 37, 39, 41, 48, 49
with streptococci, 60-62
with tyramine, 62

I

Incubation Danger Zone for enterotoxic staphylococci, 48
Inhalation of lethal gases, 146-150, 162-163 175-176.
Insulae, "suffocation as usual event" in, 145
Intoxication, ethanol, 117-122

J

Jericho, 183-184
4000 year old meats in burial chambers, 183-184
Miss Kathleen Kenyon's excavations at, 183-184
sulphur gases in this rift area, 183
Jews-Hebrews
food practices, 189-190
Passover of 64 A.D., 186-187
pork taboos, 85-91
sanitation of Jewish villages, 191
temple sacrifices, 185-188

K

Khanzir, kelb and Egyptian pigs, 86
Kilns: poisonous gases from, in Ancient Times, 149

Kings of Medes and Persians treatment of poisoners, 107 (ref. 57)
Kosher Code of Judaism, 87
　food practices, 189-190
　Maimonides' values, 190

L

Law suits, 6, 7, 24, 28-29, 40, 50, 52-53, 79, 84, 146-147, 152-154, 157-158, 168, 176, 177, 178-179, 182
Lead poisoning, 165-169
　in ancient wines, 166
　at one time from chewing snuff, 167
　ingestion of peeled lead paints: morbidity and mortality rates, 166-167
　lead fumes from burning discarded storage batteries, 167
　lead poisoning, acute and chronic, 166-167
　lead statuette of First Dynasty of Egypt, 165
　in pewter, 166
　postmortem findings, in, 166
　Roman ban on lead water pipes, 165
　salts and metal, uses in Antiquity, 165-167
　sugar of lead, 167
　symptoms of poisoning by lead and salts, 165-166
　tolerance in foods, 166
Lead shot in game and meats, 167-169
　alloy of lead and antimony, 168
　Professor Cowgill's animal feeding tests, 168
　as foreign substances in foods, 168
　monkey feeding tests, 168
Lee, Robert E., 10
　enteritis at Gettysburg, 10, 11
Leprosy and spoiled foods, 29
Luminous foods and phosphorescent bacteria, 83-84

contamination in home and store refrigerators, 83
incidence of occurrence, 83-84
isolation of these bacteria, 84
marine origins of, 83
　species, 83
observed since ancient times, 84
public health aspects, 83-84

M

Malade River outbreak, 16
Marihuana, 141-142
Mead and poisonous honey, 120-121
Mercury, 169-171
　cinnabar mined in Spain and Italy, 169
　known in Antiquity, 169
　all mercury compounds prohibited in food and drink, 170
　symptoms of poisoning, 169-170
　toxicity, 169-170
　former treatment of syphilis with, 170
Meteoric shower of November 12, 1833, 19
Mithridaticum, universal antidote, 112-115
Mountain sickness, 17-19
Mushrooms (poisonous), 128-131
　Agrippina poisons Claudius, 130
　arch poisoner Empress Agrippina, 129
　clinical types of poisoning, 128
　dried and powdered preparations, 128
　edible varieties long used as food by Babylonians and Romans, 128
　lethal species, 128
　Nero's "food of the gods", 130
　potency after 20 years storage, 128
　toxicity of *Amanita phalloides*, 128
　tragedy of Euripides of Icarus, 128-129
Mussolini, Benito: "judicial" purges with castor oil, 132
Mustard, preservation of grape must, 119

N

Napoleon
  attempted suicide with opium, 163, (ref. 92)
  murdered by arsenic poisoning, 164
  seige of Acre, 163
National Hotel Disease, 13
Neutron-activation analysis for arsenic, 164
Nicotine, 143
  American origins, 143
  cigarettes, 144
  curing of tobacco, 144
  diffusion to Old World, 144
  health hazards, 143, 144
  in *Nicotiana tabacum,* 143
  range of nicotine contents of plant, 143
  Shah Abbas' ersatz, 144
Non-food-borne causes of gastrointestinal disturbances, 77-80
Nux Vomica, 123-124
  Anthony and Cleopatra at battle of Actium, 124
  Cleopatra's "experiments" with various poisons, 124-125
  death of Cleopatra, 125
  fatal dose, 124
  fruit of Strychnos nux vomica tree, 124
  poisoning symptoms, 124
  strychnine and brucine in seeds, 124

O

Opium, 133-135
  celebrated Cave of Bats as a tomb, 133
  charitable women of Jerusalem supply merciful drug to those crucified, 134
  Martinez, Don Manuel discovered Cave of Bats in Granada, 1867, 133
  misuse of opium and derivatives, 134
  Napoleon's attempted suicide with, 163, (ref. 92)
  opium deaths of a Queen, twelve women and three warriors, 133
  opium in Neolithic Spain, 133
  suttee-like death at Ur of the Chaldees, 133
  woven esparto baskets containing opium poppy bulbs, 133
Oregon Trail, cholera outbreaks, 19
Oxalic acid poisoning, delayed rigor mortis, 98

P

Paracolon serotypes, 58-59
Passenger pigeons and disease, 23-25
  abundance of, 23
  alleged food poisoning, trial of case, 24-25
  encephalitis outbreaks, 24
  extinction, n. 10, 23-24
  salmonella in birds, 24
  viruses in Aves, 24
Pemmican, 22
Pleistocene epoch, 5
  poisoning in, 5
Poison centers in U.S.A. for treatments, 123
Poisonous natural products mistakenly used as foods, 95-100
  assay of poison in mussels, 97
  certain fish in tropical waters, 95
  fish, 95-96
  mortality rate, 97
  mussels, 96
  plants, 98
  poisonings in children from bittersweet, nightshade, laurel castor beans, black locust, cowbane, water hemlock, 96
  potato poisoning, so-called, 98-99
  rhubarb greens (oxalic acid), 98
  rigor mortis delayed in oxalic acid poisoning, 98
  symptoms in fish poisoning, 95-97
  symptoms in shellfish poisoning, 97
Posca, legionnaires' beverage, 30
Professional poisoners in Ancient Rome, 110-111

Ptomaine theory, 36

Q

Question of diamond dust as a slow poison, 154-157
Quincitilius Varus, Legate lost 21,000 Legionnaires in defeat by Arminius, 107 (ref. 58)

R

Rocky Mountain Men, 16-26
bison fat in diets, 21
buffalo meat and illness, 18, 19
cascara buckthorn in Indian wars, 20
cholera outbreaks, 19
effect of meteoric shower of 1833 on foods, 19
Francis Parkman's illness, 18
horse meat and dysenteries, 21, 22
Malade river outbreak, 16
mountain sickness, 17-19
pemmican, 22
Roman military camps, 31

S

St. Paul's illness in Galatia, 29
Salmonellae, 56-60
"Aertryke-Morseele" bacilli, 58
baked Alaska ingredients, 59
dosage, 56-57
Edgewater Beach Hotel outbreak, 59
growth at 38°-42°F, 81
human volunteer tests, 56-57
infection vs. preformed toxins, 56-57
occurrence in Nature, 57
serotypes, 56
S. typhi, 57
Sardonic smile (*risus sardonicus*), 123, 125
Shiloh battlefield, 11, 12-13
Snake handling sects, 114
Sodium fluoride, 177-180
colored blue or green to prevent accidental use as flour, etc., 178

as a household insecticide, 178
an outbreak confused with botulism, 178
symptoms in poisoning with, 178
Solanine potato poisoning — untenable, 98-99
Spanish American war camps, 31
Staphylococci, 34-56
antibiotic induced colitis, 54-55
Dr. M. A. Barber's work on *S. albus*, n. 12, 32
in cheddar cheese, 47
culture media for, 47
Dr. G. M. Dack's discoveries in 1930, 34
diagnosis, 34
enterotoxin, 34
epidemiology, 34
nature of toxin, 54
symptomology, 34
treatment, 34, 54
Dr. C. E. Dolman's description of staphylococcus intoxication, 34-35
early scepticism regarding role of staphylococci in food poisoning, 38-39
food poisoning at a wedding party, 40
human volunteers and enterotoxin, 34, 35, 37, 39, 41, 47, 48, 49
Incubation Danger Zone, 48
laudable pus, 35
Charles Lindbergh's ordeal with food poisoning, 45
monkeys as test animals, 41-42, 44
salt beef and growth of, 47-48
serological tests for enterotoxin, 44
S. roseus as enterotoxin formers, 46
Sudanese Army outbreak, 89
susceptible foods, 52-54
susceptibilities of test animals, 42-43
turkeys and dressing, culinary heating, 52
a "two bucket job", 53
typical outbreaks, 49-54

Streptococci (Lancefield type D), 60-64
   dosage producing illness, 59-62
   S. faecium, 60
   S. fecalis, 60
   human volunteer tests, 60-62
   monkey feeding tests, 62-63
   outbreak caused by, 63
   outbreak from home prepared sausage with *S. fecalis* and *Trichinella spiralis,* 93
Strychnos nux vomica, 124
Sulfites, 180-184
   color reactions in meats, 182
   in drying of fruits, 180-181
   Jericho excavations, meat found from 2000 B.C. burials, 183
   as "poor man's refrigerant", 182
   prohibited in meats, 181-182
   reduces and brightens discolored meats, 181-182
   statement by Council on Foods (AMA), 181
   toxicity and tolerances, 180-181
Sumerian milker, 36
Sumerian vase (c. 2450 B.C.) of pure antimony, 172

T

Temple meats from sacrifices, 185-191
   Apostolic Decree against blood sausages and pagan temple meats, 188-189
   bulls' blood and goats' blood as a poison, 189
   Christian rites and rites of Mithra: bulls' blood to "bless", 189
   disposal of blood, 187
   Jewish Code of Christian Jews, 188
   number of animals sacrificed, 186
   sacrifices to God, 185-187
   sacrifices to the gods, 185
   temple water supplies, 187-188
Theriac (Mithridaticum), 19, 112-115
Theriaca, Venetian "treacle", 113-114
Tombs, frozen Scythian bodies and hemp smoking equipment (500 B.C.), 142

Trials of cases, 6, 7, 24, 28-29, 40, 50, 52-53, 79, 84, 92, 93, 94, 116, 146-147, 152-154, 157-158, 168, 176, 177, 178-179, 182
Trichinosis and food taboos, 85-91
   Egyptian fish, 84
   Egyptian swine, 84, 86
   holoarctic distribution of Trichinae, 86
   newborn kid or calf in colostrum, 88-89
   origins of pork taboo in Near East, 86-88
   pork production, modern safe methods, 91-92
   St. Mark in a Venetian pork barrel, 85
   taboos and dietary laws, 85 ff.
   trichinosis outbreaks, 92-93
Turkeys, dressing, culinary heating, 52
Tyramine, 62
   Eutron® and tyramine, 62
   hypertension pressors and tyramine, 62

U

Uncertain etiologies, 81-83
   environmental temperature of host and high count milk, 80-81
   human volunteer tests with certain bacteria, 81
   milk, high-count fed to puppies, 80-81
   summer diarrhea of infants, 80
   thermophiles, mesophiles, psychrophiles, 81
Uracil in blood vessel linings enhance toxin formation by *S. aureus,* 90

V

Verdun, a German assault on, 31-32
   German Commandos felled by staphylococcus enterotoxin in sausage, 32
Viruses and "food poisoning", 73-76

Vomiting centers in laboratory animals, 42-43, 104
Vomiting and diarrhea as symptoms, 77-79
  causal agents, difficulty in determination of, 79-81
  gastrointestinal disturbances, causes, 77
  non-food poisoning entities, 77
  vomiting and diarrhea, other causes of, 77-79
  questionnaires for food poisoning investigations, 79
Voodoo deaths, 114-117
  death of Caesar Germanicus, 115-116
  death of Ramses III, 115
  "psychic arsenal" and methods in, 114-116
  successes in, 114-115

W

Wellington, Duke of, illness, 33
Wines in Ancient Times, 116-120

X

Xenophon: Claudius' Greek Coan physician, 110-111
Xenophon: remarks about poisoners in Persia, 107
  describes honey poisoning of the Ten Thousand, 120

Y

Yassa, Gengis Khan's Code on strong drink, 118

Z

Zone, incubation danger, 48